# Global Warming

Prepared by Neil McBride

This publication forms part of an Open University course S104 *Exploring science*. The complete list of texts which make up this course can be found on the back cover. Details of this and other Open University courses can be obtained from the Student Registration and Enquiry Service, The Open University, PO Box 197, Milton Keynes MK7 6BJ, United Kingdom: tel. +44 (0)845 300 60 90, email general-enquiries@open.ac.uk

Alternatively, you may visit the Open University website at http://www.open.ac.uk where you can learn more about the wide range of courses and packs offered at all levels by The Open University.

To purchase a selection of Open University course materials visit http://www.ouw.co.uk, or contact Open University Worldwide, Michael Young Building, Walton Hall, Milton Keynes MK7 6AA, United Kingdom for a brochure. tel. +44 (0)1908 858793; fax +44 (0)1908 858787; email ouw-customer-services@open.ac.uk

The Open University
Walton Hall, Milton Keynes
MK7 6AA

First published 2007

Edited and designed by The Open University.

Typeset by SR Nova Pvt Ltd, Bangalore, India.

Printed and bound in the United Kingdom by Halstan Printing Group, Amersham.

ISBN 978 1 8487 3162 2

2.1

# Contents

# Chapter 1
# Introduction

Welcome to S104 *Exploring science*. The fact that you are starting to read this book means that you are naturally curious about this planet, its history, and the life that inhabits it. No doubt you are also curious about other planets, the stars, and the galaxies that share our Universe. You are probably curious about … well, everything. If there is one subject that attempts to understand life, the Universe and (almost) everything, it is science.

The study of science helps you to understand the world around you. There may be specific things that have always puzzled you. Or perhaps you find that questions just arise naturally as you find out more. Indeed, nature seems full of wonders and full of questions – questions that, if you dig deep enough, almost always have an answer. Just for fun, here are a few questions you might like to ponder.

- Ice cubes float in a jug of water with some of the ice sticking out above the surface of the water. So why is it that when the ice melts, the level of the liquid doesn't change?
- Everything falls to the ground (given the chance) due to gravity. So why does the Earth's atmosphere not simply form a very thin layer on the ground?
- The grass and plants in a garden are mowed or cut periodically, removing a lot of organic material. However, the soil level doesn't seem to drop. So where is all the plant material coming from?

Thinking about these questions reflects what science is all about. You notice an effect or a behaviour and then ask 'Why does it do that?' Studying this course will help you to be able to answer many such questions. And the answers to these particular questions will become clear as you read this book.

While studying the eight books that form the backbone of this course, you will explore an extremely wide range of natural phenomena from a scientific point of view. You will also develop general skills that are applicable to the study and practice of science. Many of these skills are useful in all sorts of situations, so this course will help you develop in all sorts of ways. Above all, we (the S104 course team) hope you enjoy the fascinating exploration of the Universe around us.

This first book begins with a brief look at what 'science' means, and then you will start your study by considering the topic of global warming. This topic is obviously of great interest and concern, and it is an excellent place to start this course. Chapter 2 takes an introductory overview of the topic. Chapter 3 begins to consider the science in detail, starting with the observations that tell us global warming is occurring. Chapter 4 looks at just what affects the Earth's temperature so you can understand how global warming can occur. Chapters 5, 6 and 7 look at the crucial role of the atmosphere, water and carbon in global warming. Then, in Chapter 8, you will take what you have learned, and use it to predict what the global temperature might become in the future.

## 1.1   What is science?

Before you start looking at the science of global warming, take a step back for a moment and simply consider, what is science? It may seem like a rather strange question considering that you have enrolled on this course and thus must already have a good idea of what science means to you. However, your concept of what science is all about may develop throughout the course. Your understanding of what it means to approach problems in a scientific way is likely to develop too. So, it is useful to think about what science means to you at this time.

Start by considering the sort of definition you might find in a dictionary. These might include:

- the systematic study of the nature and behaviour of the material and physical Universe, based on observation, experiment and measurement
- a body of knowledge organised in a systematic manner
- a branch of knowledge or study dealing with a body of facts or truths systematically arranged and showing the operation of general laws.

Are these definitions consistent with what science means to you?

Several things are apparent from these definitions. Observation and measurement are clearly important in science. This goes back to the 'noticing an effect or a behaviour' that was mentioned earlier. It is also apparent that a 'body of knowledge' forms a large part of science. Indeed, this is perhaps the most recognisable aspect of science – scientists tend to 'know' facts and figures about all sorts of things. The way these two aspects are linked is perhaps not so obvious from these definitions.

To illustrate this, consider the difference between *observing* something as opposed to *explaining* how or why something is the way it is. In fact, both of these aspects are crucial in science, and are closely linked. An overall goal of a scientist is to understand and be able to explain some aspect of the natural world. However, this doesn't happen instantly. The first stage is to observe and record what you see. The recording process will often mean gathering data, where data might be numerical measurements (i.e. quantitative data) or descriptions and sketches (i.e. qualitative data) – indeed, any information that might be relevant. Then the scientist will look for patterns and correlations in the data, to try to make sense of what was observed (i.e. analyse the data). In doing this, some idea of how the whole system works will be developed, i.e. the scientist will have a theory about what is happening. They will then do everything they can to test whether their theory really does explain their observations. This may entail carrying out some experiments to see whether something behaves in the expected way (consistent with the theory), or to see what happens under different conditions. If the theory is successful, it should be able to predict the outcome of the experiment.

In developing an understanding about how something works, the scientist will call on all the body of knowledge that already exists about the subject. Indeed, perhaps other scientists have worked on the same problem for decades, and there are books written on the subject – it would not be sensible to try to reinvent the wheel at every stage. So the scientist uses the existing 'accepted knowledge', and builds on it. Of course, what constitutes the accepted knowledge changes and develops with time. The understanding of some topics might not have changed for decades, or even hundreds of years. For example, in Book 2 you will consider aspects of motion, where the science has been unchanged for several hundred years. If, however, the topic is more 'cutting edge' (i.e. a new field where new discoveries are being made every year), it takes time for theories to be tested, questioned and improved. New theories will become the accepted knowledge only with time.

Clearly then, in order for a scientist's new discovery or theory to become part of the accepted body of knowledge, the work must be communicated to other scientists. This is done by writing a report or a scientific article or 'paper'. A scientific paper is an article published by a specialist peer-reviewed journal. Peer-reviewed means that the manuscript has been sent to several other scientists who are experts on the topic (they are called referees), and they advise the journal editor whether the paper should be published and what specific changes and improvements must be done before this can happen. This process aims to maintain a high standard of work and tries to ensure that poor or flawed work is not published. It gives the work credibility, in that if a paper appears in a respected journal, you can be confident that the work is reliable. It is worth mentioning that this peer-review process is not infallible. Very occasionally some published work may, in time, be revealed to be wrong – indeed, there have even been cases where a person has fabricated apparently ground-breaking results. However, in general, the peer-review process ensures a consistency and reliability of published work in journals. Journals are kept in academic libraries (and are usually available online too), although arguably the two most prestigious general science journals – *Science* and *Nature* – are available as weekly magazines from a wider selection of outlets. Figure 1.1 shows a variety of scientific journals.

**Figure 1.1**    Examples of peer-reviewed scientific journals that can be found in most academic libraries, or accessed online.

Of course, unless they work in a specific field as a professional scientist, engineer or doctor, most people will never read these journals. However, you will notice when reading news items in newspapers or on web pages, that the report of some scientific work will usually say something like 'as reported in the journal *Nature* this week'. This sort of referencing of where the information comes from is extremely important. When you hear claims of amazing breakthroughs, you will be impressed if the work has been peer-reviewed and published in a respected journal. However, if the source was an anonymous person who just claimed something on their website, you would not be convinced. So the whole peer-review process is very important for maintaining credibility and reliability, even if most people leave it to others to trawl through the journals and report the most interesting science to them. Indeed, the huge body of work that appears in various scientific journals often reaches people by different routes. Publications such as *New Scientist* present all sorts of science topics in a form that is more approachable than the source journals, and newspapers generally report work in the most approachable manner of all.

The whole process described above is sometimes loosely called 'scientific method'. Throughout this course, you will follow this sort of method of observation, analysis, explanation and communication.

## 1.2    Getting started

After the brief introduction, you are no doubt keen to get started on the main topic of this book – global warming. However, before moving on, it is important that you consider a few aspects of the study ahead. First, how are you going to organise some of the practical issues of studying? These might include deciding where you intend to do most of your studying, deciding where you will keep your course materials so you can get at them easily, identifying when you are going to have significant blocks of time you can use for study, or identifying whether you are likely to have problems getting access to a computer at the times when it is most convenient.

When it comes to actual study, most of your time will be based on reading this book. That seems straightforward – it's 'simply' reading after all. However, reading in order to maximise your learning is somewhat different from much of the reading people tend to do – reading novels, magazines and so on. The material you read when you are studying will make most sense, and have the best chance of being remembered, when you actively engage with the text: in other words, when you have to respond to what is written, perhaps by answering questions or doing some tasks. To help with this, throughout the book there are occasional in-text questions (marked by coloured squares), where a question is asked and the answer is given immediately below. (The first in-text question occurs at the end of Section 2.2.) Don't simply carry on reading, but pause and think of your own answer before continuing.

There are also some numbered questions throughout the text (particularly in later books) that require a written answer. Again, do not ignore these – by answering them, you can check whether you understand the material. The answers are given at the end of the book, so you can check whether you were along the right lines. You will also be asked to do activities. These are more than single written questions and can take a variety of forms. They might ask you to calculate something, write something, carry out an experiment, or perform a computer-based (possibly online) activity. As with the in-text and numbered questions, you should tackle these activities when you come across them. However, if an activity requires a resource that you do not have immediate access to (a computer or experimental equipment for example), don't stop – carry on reading and return to the activity when it is convenient. Some of the activities have comments on them at the end of the book. You will be told when this is the case.

To help you plan your study, icons are printed in the margin of the book to indicate the activities that require you to do something, for example use a computer, connect to the internet or carry out practical work (shown, from left to right, in the margin). You will also be given guidance on the likely length of time you will need to complete activities. The actual time you take may depend on various factors, but as you work through the course you will get a feel for whether the given estimates are realistic for you personally.

This course assumes that you have some previous knowledge. However, you can revise some topics that you should remember when you see revision boxes. (These are numbered Box 2.1, etc.) You may not need to read these boxes or you may find them extremely helpful – you will have to judge.

The terms given in **bold** type within the book are key terms. You will find definitions of these terms in the course Glossary. These are terms that we expect you to be able to explain the meaning of, and use correctly, throughout the course.

The greatest challenge in learning from a book is to try to engage with the text in the way that questions or activities force you to do, even when it is just plain text. You can do this by active reading.

## 1.2.1    Active reading

When reading a lot of text, it can be easy to fall into a form of reading more appropriate to reading a novel or magazine. The text can wash over you, such that, even though it is all very interesting at the time, it can be hard to remember facts and concepts later. The way to avoid this is to read actively by trying to interact with the text. For example, use highlighter pens to emphasise points you think are important or interesting – perhaps key concepts or facts that you might want to return to later. Note this means that you will write or draw on your book, which you would not normally do when reading. However, this book forms an important part of your learning experience, and you have to customise the book in a way that best serves your learning. Highlighting or underlining can help you to remember what you have read. Indeed, the process of thinking about which bits of text are worth highlighting makes you engage with the material.

Making additional notes as you go along, or summarising sections, can be an excellent way to ensure you understand the material. After all, if you cannot summarise or explain it to yourself, you probably need to revisit it. Sometimes drawing sketches or diagrams to represent ideas can be helpful – even just writing down individual words can help you to remember them and embed them in your mind (similarly, some people repeat the name of a person they have just been introduced to, in order to help them remember the name). You may find it helpful to add notes, in your own words, for glossary terms, to aid your understanding. Any notes can form part of your study folder. A study folder is simply a way of gathering together all the material you have generated during your study: for example, notes, answers to questions, activity work, graphs you have plotted or diagrams you have drawn, commentary on your progress. Your study folder may actually be a workbook with notes written in it and items stuck in it, or a collection of electronic documents, or a mixture of both. Whatever form it takes, a study folder will become an excellent resource for revision, and for reminding you of what you have learned.

It is worth mentioning that making useful notes is a skill that needs developing. If you are new to it, the greatest difficulty is deciding how much to note down – often the danger is to write too much, or to simply copy from the book. Notes are most effective when they are in your own words and just highlight the important concepts and facts, so you can return to them and digest them quickly and easily later.

All these approaches are examples of active reading and you are *strongly* encouraged to do this sort of active reading throughout the rest of this course.

### 1.2.2    Making time for your study

The first activity involves planning your study time over the coming weeks allocated to Book 1.

### Activity 1.1    Planning your study of Book 1

We expect this activity will take you approximately 30 minutes.

One of the most important outcomes of this activity is to identify times that you can set aside for study, taking account of specific tasks that require a computer or carrying out some practical work or, indeed, any personal time constraints.

In terms of periods of time given over to study, some people find that little and often is a good approach. However, others prefer to work in fewer but longer periods. For many people, weekends are the most sensible time to study. You should follow whatever is the best approach for you – and you may find this develops as you progress through the course.

The best place to start this planning activity is with the course Study Calendar. This indicates the pacing of study throughout the weeks allocated to this book. It is also a guide to activities that require a computer, online access or practical work. For example, in Book 1, Activity 8.1 requires a computer and Activities 1.1, 3.1, 7.3, 8.2 and 8.3 require a computer and online access. Furthermore, the Study Calendar on the course website identifies when it is appropriate to work on assessment material. Using this information, you can then construct your own *personal* timetable that has day-to-day details of when you intend to study. In essence, your timetable will resemble that shown in Table 1.1. This is the most basic, blank template that you could use as a guide. However, you will find an electronic template of a similar timetable grid on the course website.

**Table 1.1** An example of a timetable grid that would allow you to plan your study for three weeks. (An electronic version of a similar grid is available on the course website.)

| Day of week: | Saturday | Sunday | Monday | Tuesday | Wednesday | Thursday | Friday |
|---|---|---|---|---|---|---|---|
| Week 1 | | | | | | | |
| Week 2 | | | | | | | |
| Week 3 | | | | | | | |

Now go to Activity 1.1 on the course website, to access the timetable template and, guided by the Study Calendar, begin filling in your personal study timetable.

Note that, about half-way through this book, you will be asked to think about (i.e. to *reflect on*) whether you managed to stick to your planned timetable, or whether you had to modify it as you went along. Most importantly, you will use what you have learned from this first experience of planning and then doing your study to consider how you can modify and improve the process for later books.

## 1.3   Summary of Chapter 1

Scientific investigation tends to follow a process of observation, analysis, explanation and communication.

In order to test an explanation, experiments may be carried out to see whether something behaves the way that is expected (or to see how it behaves in unfamiliar conditions).

Scientific ideas and theories can be developed, modified or even completely changed over time.

Scientific ideas will eventually only become part of an accepted body of knowledge if the ideas are communicated appropriately, such as in peer-reviewed journals.

It is useful to make a detailed plan of how and when you will be able to study, and to then reflect on whether the plan is successful.

# Chapter 2
# Global warming – an interdisciplinary issue

Global warming refers to the increasing temperature of the Earth's atmosphere. This issue cannot have escaped anyone's attention, and it is likely to remain a major issue for the foreseeable future. However, understanding this topic is far from easy – the Earth's climate is extremely complicated. Furthermore, if a person's only exposure to the science of global warming has been through the general media (news stories, etc.) then it may be difficult for them to get a view of what is really going on. Arguments about whether the Earth really is or is not warming up, and the causes of any effect, are now on many political and economic agendas. Some groups deny the existence of global warming, or at least any relationship with human activity on the planet, while other groups might be accused of scaremongering. There is no question that global warming has become a fascinating topic regardless of the science behind it.

This book will explore in some detail the science behind global warming. The science is truly interdisciplinary, i.e. issues that need to be considered use knowledge and understanding that might typically be described as physics, or chemistry, or Earth sciences, or environmental sciences, or biology – or even astronomy. This book touches on all these scientific disciplines to some extent. (You might even choose to study global warming and climate change in greater detail in higher-level courses with The Open University.)

So, first you will briefly consider the overall 'big picture'.

## 2.1    Rumours of catastrophe

No doubt you have seen newspaper or magazine articles, web pages, television programmes or news reports about the issues surrounding global warming. Understandably, many of these stories focus on the potential effects of a rise in the Earth's temperature. Figure 2.1 shows a few such headlines which could give you the impression that the world is facing some sort of global catastrophe.

The overall concept of higher temperatures caused by global warming, and the idea that global warming could have many uncomfortable consequences, is already embedded in popular culture. Indeed, whenever an unusual weather event occurs, many people might wonder whether it is a consequence of global warming. It may be a particularly powerful storm, or a large number of hurricanes in one particular year, or a headline such as 'hottest July on record' – whatever it is, it can be tempting to blame global warming. However, care must be taken not to jump to conclusions. Figure 2.2 shows the damage caused by a tornado that struck a small area of the city of Birmingham in the UK in July 2005. For some people, tornados are not uncommon: for example, those living on the plains of the mid-west USA. However, most UK residents would be extremely surprised to see a tornado coming their way. Was this apparently unusual weather event a consequence of global warming? In fact, very small

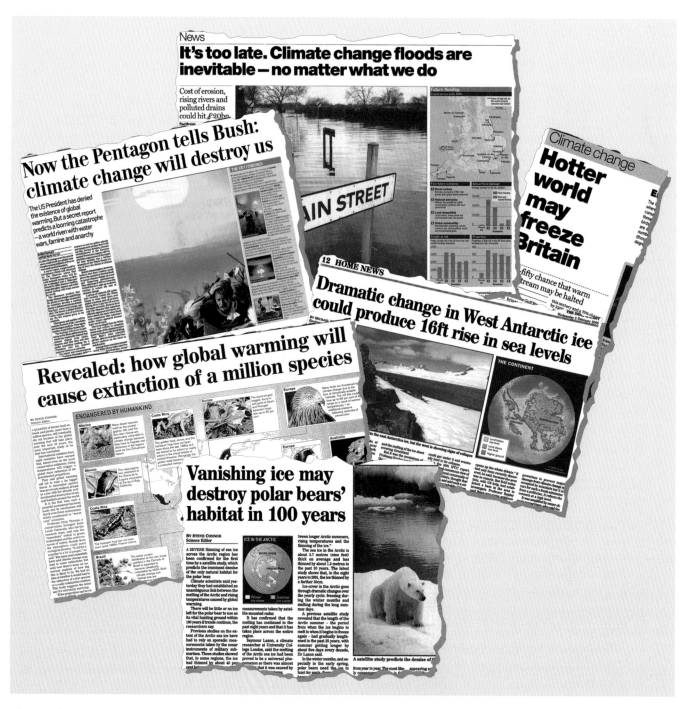

**Figure 2.1**   Cuttings from newspaper stories focusing on some of the more extreme consequences of global warming.

tornados are not uncommon in the UK. Usually they are weak and relatively benign; few will do any damage to buildings for example. However, if you wait long enough, the more powerful 'extreme event' will happen eventually, just as if you throw five dice repeatedly for long enough, eventually you will get five sixes (Figure 2.3).

**Figure 2.2**   Photograph showing considerable damage to houses caused by a tornado in an area of the UK's second largest city, Birmingham, in July 2005.

**Figure 2.3**   If you wait long enough, you too could roll five sixes (although, admittedly it may take a while – on average you will get five sixes every 8000 or so rolls). So, the unlikely event does occasionally happen.

Having said that, some unusual weather events may well be linked to an overall global effect. The point is that it is hard to untangle the extreme event from the overall slow, gradual underlying changes. To get to the bottom of long-term changes usually means looking at the *average* behaviour over long periods of time. You will do this for temperature in Chapter 3.

However, it is easier to see some effects more than others. Figure 2.4 shows the spectacular, and worryingly rapid, retreat of a major ice shelf on the Antarctic peninsula. In 2002, an area of 3200 km² (an area greater than that of Luxembourg) disintegrated in just 35 days. Indeed, the total loss from seven ice shelves between 1974 and 2002 amounted to an area of 17 500 km² (an area the size of Kuwait). This ice disintegration is unquestionably caused by the warming that has occurred in the region over the last few decades. (Note that, when describing an area of land, units such as km² or kilometres squared are used. The use of units is described in Box 2.1 (overleaf), which you should read now if you need a reminder.)

Some direct consequences of higher global temperatures are conceptually obvious: droughts, famines, a change of ecosystems (i.e. the combined system of land, local climate and the plants and animals of a region), a change in the agricultural crops that can be grown in a particular region, etc. A less obvious, although heavily publicised, consequence is rising sea level. The Intergovernmental Panel on Climate Change (IPCC), in their Third Assessment Report published in 2001, said that by 2100 the average global sea level is likely to rise by between 0.09 m and 0.88 m. Some estimates are even higher than this.

**Figure 2.4**   Satellite image of a region, about 200 km across, of the Larsen-B ice shelf on the east side of the Antarctic peninsula. The red curve shows the extent of the ice shelf in 1995; the other curves show the extent of the rapid retreat during 2002.

## Box 2.1  Using units

The majority of quantities have units associated with them. Without the units, a measurement doesn't mean much. Everyone uses units in everyday life: for example, a price is measured in pounds (or euros or dollars, etc.), fuel is in litres (or gallons), height is in metres (or feet and inches). In science, certain quantities have specific units. These favoured units are called **SI units** (SI is an abbreviation of *Le Système International d'Unités* or International System of Units). For example, the SI unit of distance is the metre (m), the SI unit of mass is the kilogram (kg) and the SI unit of time is the second (s). That said, everyone breaks the rules sometimes: although it is in common use, °C is not the SI unit for temperature! (You will meet the proper unit in Book 3.)

To ensure the units work out correctly within calculations, you should always include the units for each quantity within the calculation. So, for example, if a rectangular garden has sides 5 m and 6 m long, the area is calculated by multiplying the two lengths, so you write

$$\text{area} = 5 \text{ m} \times 6 \text{ m}$$

This is equivalent to $(5 \times 6) \, (\text{m} \times \text{m}) = 30 \text{ m}^2$. Similarly, a cube with sides 3 m long has a volume of $3 \text{ m} \times 3 \text{ m} \times 3 \text{ m} = 27 \text{ m}^3$. This process is also followed when dividing quantities and their units. For example, speed (which tends to be quoted as miles or kilometres per hour) is generally distance per unit of time: in other words, distance divided by time. So a speed might be calculated as:

$$\text{speed} = \frac{\text{distance}}{\text{time}} = \frac{20 \text{ m}}{2 \text{ s}} = 10 \, \frac{\text{m}}{\text{s}} = 10 \text{ m s}^{-1}$$

where m denotes metres and s denotes seconds. Note that $\frac{\text{m}}{\text{s}}$ became m s$^{-1}$, i.e. $\frac{1}{\text{s}}$ became s$^{-1}$. This is because one over a quantity (e.g. a number or, in this case, the unit s) can be written as that quantity raised to the power of $-1$. So:

$$\frac{\text{m}}{\text{s}} = \text{m} \times \frac{1}{\text{s}} = \text{m} \times \text{s}^{-1} \quad \text{i.e. m s}^{-1}$$

Of course, some quantities do not have units, i.e. they are said to be dimensionless. This is the case when using ratios. A ratio of two numbers might be written as, for example, 2 : 1. However all ratios can also be written as fractions, with the individual values including the units. The : symbol indicates dividing the first quantity by the second quantity. For example, for an adult of height 2.0 m, and a child of height 1.0 m, the ratio of the values of the heights is given by:

$$\text{ratio of heights} = \frac{2.0 \text{ m}}{1.0 \text{ m}} = 2.0 \, \frac{\text{m}}{\text{m}} = 2.0$$

i.e. the final answer 2.0 is dimensionless, and indeed all ratios are dimensionless for this reason.

**Figure 2.5**   Diagram of the coastal regions of Bangladesh, showing the present-day coastline, and how far the sea would inundate the land (dashed line) if a large rise in sea level (about 1.5 m) occurred over the next 200 years.

These sea-level rises would inevitably cause significant inundation of many coastal regions. Figure 2.5 shows the possible effect for a country that is likely to suffer some of the worst consequences – Bangladesh. Over the next 200 years, a sea-level rise of 1.5 m is possible, which would rob Bangladesh of much of its most highly populated and productive regions.

Although the overall loss of coastal regions is very gradual, the effect can have severe consequences on short timescales. This is because the severe consequences to local populations arise from relatively infrequent flooding, caused by major storms or sustained high levels of rainfall. During storms, high winds approaching land can cause major storm surges which cause temporary high local sea levels, and drive this 'extra' seawater a long way inland by breaching any sea defences or through the surges travelling inland via rivers (which then burst their banks). Such an event occurred in New Orleans, USA, in August 2005 during hurricane Katrina.

Storm surges or flooding from rivers are not new phenomena of course. However these events, coupled with a gradual sea-level rise and increasing population numbers in coastal cities and their surrounding areas, make the likely social and economic consequences of the occasional extreme event worse than has been experienced in the past. This is particularly true of economically poor regions that have not built sea defences. Furthermore, when the waters subside, people inevitably return to the region they know (which is often agriculturally fertile land) and attempt to carry on their lives as before.

When considering that the vulnerability to storm surges and flooding can extend quite a long way inland, you realise that a sea-level rise will not just change the apparent coastline. Large areas will be at risk of occasional flooding, particularly regions that are currently less than 5 m above sea level. These regions are shown for mainland Britain in Figure 2.6.

**Figure 2.6** Map of mainland Britain showing the regions (dark areas) that are currently less than 5 m above sea level, and are thus at risk of occasional flooding from sea storm surges.

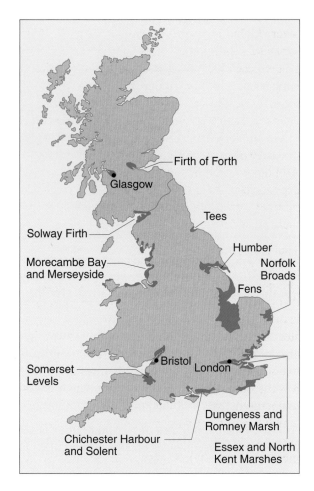

All the consequences of global warming will cause changes in ecosystems. Animals may be particularly hard hit in some areas. Many populations will dwindle or die out. Simply adapting to the new climatic conditions may not be an option for some animals, as food sources may disappear. This will result in a change in the distributions of animal populations. Some areas that supported one species might be no longer suitable, whereas another area which was previously unsuitable might become habitable. The end result is that some animal populations will essentially move geographically, and survive as a species. However, animals that rely on a particular aspect of the climate in order to find food will probably dwindle in numbers, and perhaps become extinct. This may be the fate of polar bears, which hunt on the Arctic ice sheets.

## 2.2  The greenhouse effect – an introduction

Global warming appears to be happening and the consequences are far reaching but what is causing it? Answering that question is the major focus of this book but, even before looking at the details, you probably already know the most general answer – the 'greenhouse effect'.

You will look at the processes behind the greenhouse effect later in this book but, for now, it is enough to think of the greenhouse effect as being an increase in the temperature of the environment caused by the Earth's atmosphere 'trapping' heat. The name of the effect comes from the analogy of a garden greenhouse, where higher temperatures can be maintained inside the greenhouse than in the surrounding environment. In fact, the physical reason for the Earth's atmospheric greenhouse effect is *not* the same as that which contributes to the major temperature rise in a garden greenhouse (you will see why in Chapter 4) – thus the effect is perhaps poorly named. None the less, the overall concept that the air is hotter than might be expected, as in a greenhouse, is reasonable. The ability of the atmosphere to trap heat and maintain a greenhouse effect depends on the presence of particular gases in the atmosphere: the so-called greenhouse gases. And the *level* of the greenhouse effect (i.e. the size of the increase in temperature) depends broadly on the amounts of greenhouse gases in the atmosphere. So, the more of a greenhouse gas there is in the atmosphere, the more greenhouse effect there is, and thus the warmer it gets.

That is not quite the same as saying that any observed warming must have been caused by an increase in the amount of one or more greenhouse gases in the atmosphere. The Earth's climate is a complex system and there are many factors that can affect temperatures, but the level of greenhouse gases in the atmosphere is one very important factor. Furthermore, while the Earth's temperature has been steadily rising over the last 200 years (as you will see in Chapter 3), there has also been a steady increase in the level of greenhouse gases in the atmosphere. A major push of scientific research in recent times has been to determine whether it is the increase in the level of greenhouse gases that has *caused* the increase in temperature. Much of the work to determine this has relied on computing power, which has improved enormously over the past 20 years. While initial work struggled to establish with reasonable confidence the causal link between the increase in greenhouse gases and the increase in temperature, it is now possible to say beyond reasonable doubt that the increase in temperature is caused by the increase in greenhouse gases. This realisation is so important because at least some of the rise in greenhouse gas levels comes from human activity. So, humans are contributing to global warming and thus experiencing some level of human-induced, or **anthropogenic**, climate change.

## 2.2.1    Carbon dioxide

The main greenhouse gas that is derived from human activity is carbon dioxide. Other greenhouses gases are also important, such as methane, nitrous oxide, and various complex carbon-based chemicals. (You needn't worry if you are not familiar with these chemicals.) However, the sheer amount of carbon dioxide produced by human activity means that the anthropogenic contribution to the greenhouse effect is dominated by carbon dioxide. Carbon dioxide is produced in various ways, but the major emissions are from burning fossil fuels, i.e. oil, coal and natural gas. Figure 2.7 shows the proportion of different sources leading to anthropogenic emission of carbon dioxide. This information is displayed as a

**Figure 2.7**   The proportion of different sources leading to anthropogenic emission of carbon dioxide in 2004. The data are plotted as a pie chart, where the size of a slice indicates the proportion of the total: 96% of all carbon dioxide emissions comes from burning fossil fuels.

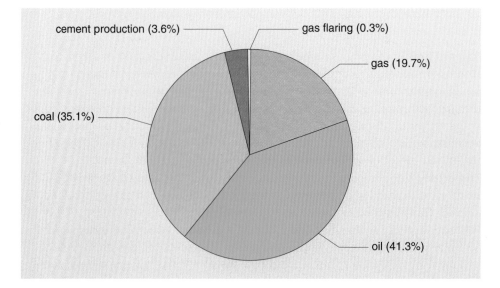

**pie chart**, where the size of a slice of the pie indicates the proportion of the total. For example, if the pie was cut into four equal slices, each slice would represent one-quarter of the total, or 25%. You can see from Figure 2.7 that the burning of oil-based products accounts for the major contribution (41.3% of the total), although it is closely followed by the use of coal (35.1%). 96.4% of all carbon dioxide emissions comes from burning fossil fuels.

Question 2.1

Is the proportion of carbon dioxide emissions resulting from the burning of oil-based products nearer to one-quarter or one-half of the total emissions? (Once you have attempted this question, check your answer with the one at the back of the book before moving on.)

Often the carbon dioxide emissions are described in terms of the total mass of carbon added to the atmosphere. In 2004, the total mass of anthropogenic carbon emission was estimated at 7300 million tonnes, where a tonne (sometimes called a metric ton) is 1000 kg. So, 7300 million tonnes is 7300 000 000 000 kg. There were 13 countries that emitted over 100 million tonnes of carbon each, accounting for 67% of the entire world's emission. Figure 2.8 shows the global distribution of carbon emissions as a pie chart, and Table 2.1 shows the actual data used. Note that, in Table 2.1, the units of the values (million tonnes and percentage respectively) are shown in the column headings and are written as '/million tonnes' and '/%'. If this notation is not familiar to you, read Box 2.2 now.

■   You can see from Table 2.1 that the USA and China were the major contributors of atmospheric carbon in 2004. Did the emissions from the USA and China combined account for the majority of the world's carbon emission in that year?

☐   No, the USA and China combined accounted for about 37% of the world's carbon emission, i.e. the rest of the world's countries accounted for about 63% of the total emission.

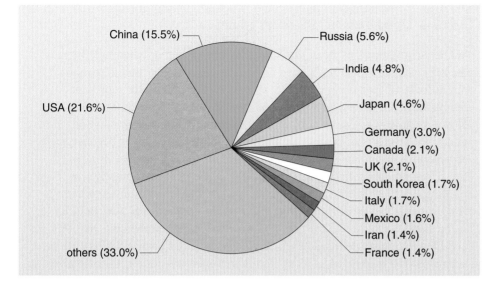

**Figure 2.8**   Pie chart showing the proportion of carbon emitted globally into the atmosphere in 2004. The pie chart has 14 slices, with 13 slices representing the 13 countries that emitted more than 100 million tonnes of carbon each, and the remaining slice representing the contributions from all other countries combined. The 13 specified countries account for 67.0% of the world's total carbon emission.

**Table 2.1**   Anthropogenic emissions of carbon dioxide into the atmosphere in 2004, expressed in terms of the mass of carbon in millions of tonnes, and their proportions of the total world emissions. Countries that emitted over 100 million tonnes of carbon are listed individually. (You may have noted that the percentage values actually add up to 100.1%. This is because the individual values are only quoted to the nearest 0.1%, and this leads to what is known as a rounding error.)

| Country | Mass of carbon/million tonnes | Proportion of total world emissions/% |
|---|---|---|
| USA | 1580 | 21.6 |
| China | 1130 | 15.5 |
| Russia | 407 | 5.6 |
| India | 347 | 4.8 |
| Japan | 336 | 4.6 |
| Germany | 220 | 3.0 |
| Canada | 154 | 2.1 |
| UK | 152 | 2.1 |
| South Korea | 124 | 1.7 |
| Italy | 122 | 1.7 |
| Mexico | 114 | 1.6 |
| Iran | 104 | 1.4 |
| France | 104 | 1.4 |
| All other countries | 2410 | 33.0 |

Question 2.2

Using the data in Table 2.1, what is the ratio of the UK's carbon emission to that of the major contributor, the USA?

Box 2.2  Using units in tables and graphs

When writing units in the column headings of tables, or when labelling the axes of graphs, the units need to be labelled in a way that is perhaps not initially obvious. For example, an axis on a graph might represent temperature, and many people would label this axis 'temperature (°C)'. However, this is not quite correct. The SI **convention** (i.e. an adopted rule that is followed) is to label this axis 'temperature/°C'. This is because the '/' represents a division sign, so essentially this is saying 'temperature ÷ °C'. So, if you are about to plot a point of, say, 22 °C, you are actually plotting 22 °C ÷ °C = 22. Thus you plot a dimensionless number, which is reasonable as you don't want to plot a point and write °C next to it. It is the same for tables: in the column heading, you write the units as '/°C', and then the numbers that are written in the table are dimensionless. If this seems hard to understand, simply remember the convention: for example, use /°C and not (°C). Thus the column headings in Table 2.1 are written as /million tonnes and /%. You will become familiar with this notation as you study this and later books.

Assuming that anthropogenic-driven global warming should preferably be avoided, a reduction in carbon emissions is required. However, reducing carbon emissions in a world with a growing population, and rapidly developing industrial regions, is a real challenge. Efforts to reduce carbon emissions over the next few decades will be crucial in determining the climatic conditions that humans will have to contend with over the next few centuries. You will return to considering future carbon emissions and resulting temperature rises in Chapter 8.

## 2.3    Precipitation

So far, this chapter has concentrated on carbon dioxide, as it is the major anthropogenic greenhouse gas. It may surprise you to learn, however, that carbon dioxide is not the most abundant greenhouse gas in the atmosphere. That honour belongs to water vapour. Indeed, water has a crucial role to play in determining the temperature of the Earth. You will consider water, and how it cycles through different environments, in Chapter 6. One of the more obvious natural mechanisms to transfer water around the globe is clouds. Cloud formation often leads to rainfall, and this rainfall feeds rivers that eventually deposit their water into lakes, seas and oceans. Rain keeps the Earth's land masses irrigated. Of course, it isn't just rain that falls. Hail, snow, dew and frost are other ways of precipitating water out of the atmosphere. Indeed, to cover all these eventualities, **precipitation** is used instead of rainfall. For most people, for most of the time, precipitation is just a fancy word for rainfall. However, if you live in one of the colder regions on Earth, most precipitation might be in the form of snow.

In this course, you will study mainly through the books and computer-based activities. However, there will also be a practical component to your studies,

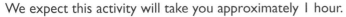

and you should start the first practical activity now (or when it is convenient for you – you scheduled it in your study timetable, which you produced in Activity 1.1). The activity relates to the topic of precipitation and we hope it will be good fun as well as demonstrating several scientific techniques and good practice.

## Activity 2.1   Measuring precipitation – Part I

We expect this activity will take you approximately I hour.

In this first practical activity, you will measure your local precipitation (probably rainfall) by making a pair of simple rain gauges and using them to record precipitation throughout the next two weeks. It will help you to think about the design of an experimental apparatus, how to gather data reliably, the uncertainties and errors that might creep into the process, how to do some basic analysis, and how to present your results to other people most effectively.

You might live in a very dry area and be fairly sure that there won't be any rainfall over the next two weeks. This doesn't matter: designing and making the rain gauge is still good experience. After all, are you absolutely sure that there won't be some moisture or dew which might condense into the rain gauge during the night, or an unexpected period of rain? Whatever your local climatic conditions, you should try it. It is important to appreciate that, when gathering precipitation data, a result of zero rainfall is just as important as any other result. Indeed, it would be a great failing in scientific method if people only recorded and reported to others when something happened. Often it is just as significant when something does *not* happen.

You will be able to discuss the design and siting of your rain gauge with other students in your online tutor group forum. After you have gathered your data and calculated your results (towards the end of Book 1) you will be expected to post these results to your tutor group forum and to discuss the reasons for similarities and differences with your fellow students in the forum.

If you are unable to do this activity for any reason, you should ask your tutor for advice.

### Aims

The main aim of this activity is to introduce designing practical work, making measurements, and recording and analysing data. It should also help you to understand:

- how precipitation is measured
- the concept of a mean
- the uncertainties involved with measurements
- the variability in quoted mean values.

### Introduction

The activity involves constructing a rain gauge and measuring precipitation in order to calculate the mean daily precipitation over two weeks.

*How precipitation is reported*

Weather reports tend to give the amount of precipitation in units of length, usually millimetres, abbreviated to mm. At first this may seem strange because you might expect that the amount of rain, or other forms of precipitation, should be measured as a volume. However, what is being reported is the depth of rain that falls on the Earth's surface in a location. Suppose you monitored the amount of rain that fell in one day on one square kilometre of a perfectly flat region of the Earth's surface. Assuming that the rain does not run off the surface and out of this area, is not absorbed into the ground, and does not evaporate, a pool of water with an area of one square kilometre (1 km²) would be formed. The depth of this pool would be a measure of the amount of rain that fell on that area in one day.

■   Consider Figure 2.9, which shows a pool of 1 square kilometre. Assuming that the rain fell uniformly over this square kilometre, would the depth of rainfall be any different if it was measured over one square metre or a circle 10 mm across?

☐   You would be looking at smaller pools with very different volumes of water but, in each case, the depth would be the same, as shown in Figure 2.9.

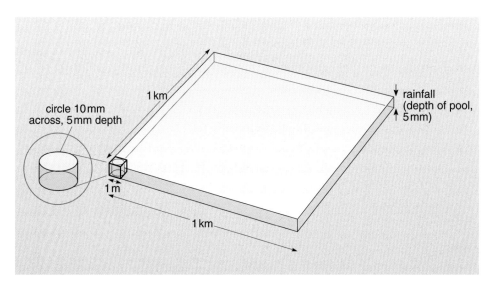

**Figure 2.9**   Pools of one square kilometre, one square metre and a circular area 10 mm across, containing water to a depth of 5 mm (not to scale).

So, quoting the precipitation as a depth gives a measure of the amount of water that has fallen in a particular region, and this measure is independent of the size of the area on which the water has fallen.

Practical procedure

**Safety Warning**

Read the whole of this section before starting the activity and make sure that you have read the section on 'Practical activities' in the *Course Guide*.

When carrying out practical activities, you should always take care to observe the simple safety precautions highlighted in the course book.

Very often, as in the case of this activity, these precautions will seem quite obvious and just a matter of using common sense. However that does not mean that you should ignore the safety instructions. The Open University has a duty to give advice on health and safety to students carrying out any activities that are described in the course. Similarly, *you* have a duty to follow the instructions and to carry out the practical activity having regard for your own safety and that of other people around you. Whenever you do practical activities you should think about the hazards involved, and how any risks can be minimised.

**Important safety precautions**

Take note of the following safety precautions, which apply to all practical activities:

- Keep children and animals away while you are working.
- Clear your working area of clutter. Put all food away. Ensure there is nothing to trip on underfoot.
- Always wash your hands thoroughly after a practical activity.
- Any household items used should be thoroughly cleaned before returning them to domestic use.

In addition, you should note the following precautions specific to this activity:

- Take care when cutting any materials (plastic bottles for example), especially if using a naked blade.
- When choosing vessels to act as the collecting containers in the rain gauges, choose vessels that do not have sharp edges which might be a hazard when being handled (for example, avoid using a opened 'tin can' with sharp edges).
- When siting your rain gauges, ensure you do not site them where they might be a trip hazard.
- Try to ensure that animals or children do not have access to the rain gauges, and particularly be aware if children might be able to drink the contents of the rain gauges.
- If siting your gauge in contact with soil, take care to avoid contact with soil, particularly through cuts and grazes on your hands.

*Task 1  Thinking about design*

Spend a few minutes thinking about how you will measure the mean daily precipitation over two weeks. You should consider each of the following questions before looking at the comments on this activity (at the back of this book).

(a)  What type of collecting vessel will you use for the rain gauge? Should it have a particular size and shape? Does it need some form of cover?

(b)  Where will you site the rain gauge?

(c) How will you measure the amount of precipitation?

(d) How often will you record the data? Should you empty the rain gauge after each measurement?

(e) What problems might you have in measuring the precipitation?

You should now look at the comments on Task 1 at the end of this book before continuing with the activity.

### Task 2 Constructing the rain gauges

You should now construct two rain gauges: one from an open-topped, straight-sided, flat-bottomed container (Gauge 1), and the second with a funnel in the top (Gauge 2). Plastic bottles supply useful construction materials, and the top part of a plastic bottle makes an ideal funnel. The use of two different rain gauges will demonstrate whether losses through evaporation are significant.

■ Why should the area of the mouth of the funnel of Gauge 2 match the area of the bottom of the vessel?

☐ The rain gauge collects water over an area defined by the mouth of the funnel, so you need to measure the depth of a pool of water that matches this area.

■ Must the two rain gauges have the same collecting area?

☐ No: as mentioned earlier, the depth of the precipitation is the same irrespective of the area that you choose for the measurement – provided that the area of the mouth of the rain gauge matches the area of the base.

Having constructed your gauges, you should set them up in your chosen location. You are now ready to start recording data.

There are no comments on this task.

### Obtaining data

### Task 3 Recording the data

Ideally, you should record, each day, the amount of precipitation over the previous 24 hours. Enter the measurements into Table 2.2. The best way to do this is to measure the depth of the water in the two rain gauges each day at a particular time. Record the date of the reading in row 1, the time of the reading in row 2, and the depths you measure for Gauge 1 and Gauge 2 in rows 3 and 5, respectively. You will deal with the other two rows later.

When you record the data, you will no doubt use a ruler at some point, which will probably have 1 mm graduations on it. When you make your measurements, you should try to record the depth to the *nearest* 0.5 mm (i.e. *half* a graduation). So, if you see a level that is some way between (for instance) 6 mm and 7 mm, you can decide whether you think it is nearest to 6.0 mm, 6.5 mm or 7.0 mm. (This is explained in Chapter 3.) If for some reason you can't make a measurement on a particular day, it does not make the results void – the gauges are still accumulating precipitation whether you look at them or not!

There are no comments on this task.

**Table 2.2** Precipitation measurements each day for week 1 and week 2.

| Week 1 date | | | | | | | |
|---|---|---|---|---|---|---|---|
| Time of recording | | | | | | | |
| Depth in Gauge 1/mm | | | | | | | |
| Precipitation in previous 24 hours from Gauge 1/mm | | | | | | | |
| Depth in Gauge 2/mm | | | | | | | |
| Precipitation in previous 24 hours from Gauge 2/mm | | | | | | | |

Gauge 1: mean daily precipitation for week 1 ................. (You will calculate this in Chapter 4.)

Gauge 2: mean daily precipitation for week 1 ................. (You will calculate this in Chapter 4.)

| Week 2 date | | | | | | | |
|---|---|---|---|---|---|---|---|
| Time of recording | | | | | | | |
| Depth in Gauge 1/mm | | | | | | | |
| Precipitation in previous 24 hours from Gauge 1/mm | | | | | | | |
| Depth in Gauge 2/mm | | | | | | | |
| Precipitation in previous 24 hours from Gauge 2/mm | | | | | | | |

Gauge 1: mean daily precipitation for week 2 ................. (You will calculate this in Chapter 8.)

Gauge 2: mean daily precipitation for week 2 ................. (You will calculate this in Chapter 8.)

You will revisit this activity at the end of Chapter 4 – by when you will probably have gathered your first week of data and can start analysing the results. There are no comments on this task.

## 2.4   Summary of Chapter 2

The Earth is currently undergoing global warming, which is caused by the greenhouse effect.

The greenhouse effect arises from the presence of greenhouse gases in the atmosphere.

The major greenhouse gas in the atmosphere is water vapour. However, the major anthropogenic greenhouse gas (i.e. the main greenhouse gas produced by human activity) is carbon dioxide.

Pie charts can be used to display data, where the size of each slice of the pie chart represents the proportion of the total.

In studying this chapter, you have made sense of information displayed in images and diagrams, and data presented in tables and pie charts. You have encountered various units, and seen how to include units in table headings. You have considered aspects of experimental design, and started to make and record measurements.

# Chapter 3
# The Earth's surface temperature

Following the overview in Chapter 2, you will now explore the details of the science of global warming. You will follow the scientific method of observation, analysis, explanation and communication, so the place to start is with the observations at the heart of the topic of global warming – temperature. Other aspects of temperature that will be considered throughout the rest of the book are how it is measured, how it is affected by the atmosphere, and how it has changed over time and is likely to change in the near future.

## 3.1    Measuring temperature

When considering the topic of global warming, the change in temperature of the environment must obviously be included. How might this be done? If someone occasionally glanced at a thermometer in their garden and suspected that the temperature was higher than they remember it being about the same time last year, would that be grounds for concluding that there is global warming? No – you would want to know much more about how the temperature varied over many years, how the measurements were taken, at what time of day, etc. Clearly, the recording of temperature is an important thing to get right.

### 3.1.1    Measurements

Although surface temperature is often referred to, it doesn't mean the temperature of the ground. The phrase refers to the temperature of the atmosphere just above the surface. So how might that be measured? 'Just stick a thermometer in the air' is not an adequate answer. The temperature near the ground varies with height and, therefore, a few centimetres above the ground it can be several degrees different from, say, a metre above the ground.

■   What factors could affect the measurement of temperature?

☐   Direct sunlight would tend to warm the thermometer and give a higher reading than it should. Being open to rain might affect temperature, as the rain might be cooler than the air near the ground. Even a shaded thermometer may be problematic – if it was sited at a location that caught the Sun (because of reflective surfaces nearby or little air flow) then the local air temperature might be higher than that of the surrounding area.

The essence of obtaining measurements is to place a thermometer (or other temperature-recording device – often an electronic device attached to a computer) in a well-ventilated box in an open space about a metre above the ground (e.g. Figure 3.1). Every day, at set times, the temperature of the air is recorded. This temperature is then regarded as the **Earth's surface temperature** at that location, at the time of measurement.

Of course, the temperatures recorded will depend in some way on the time of day the readings are taken. So, if you are concerned with getting a representative

**Figure 3.1**   A box, known as a Stevenson screen, which allows ventilation but screens the enclosed instruments from direct sunlight and rain.

temperature value for a given day (i.e. 24-hour period), you must calculate an average, or a mean, temperature. The idea of averaging is to give a single value that best represents a fluctuating quantity, such as the temperature at a given location. In everyday speech, the word average can be used to describe any typical or characteristic attribute of something. However, this is a loose definition and can sometimes lead to confusion over exactly what is meant. To overcome this problem, scientists define the term **mean** as the sum of a series of measurements divided by the number of those measurements.

To take a real example, Table 3.1 shows the 24 hourly surface temperature readings from 00.00 (midnight) to 23.00 (11 p.m.) taken on a summer's day in Milton Keynes, UK. The units of temperature used here are degrees Celsius (°C).

**Table 3.1**  The temperature every hour from 00.00 (midnight) to 23.00 (11 p.m.) on a summer's day in Milton Keynes, UK. Note that temperatures have been recorded to the nearest 0.5 °C.

| Time/hours | Temperature/°C | Time/hours | Temperature/°C |
|---|---|---|---|
| 00.00 | 16.0 | 12.00 | 19.0 |
| 01.00 | 16.0 | 13.00 | 19.5 |
| 02.00 | 15.0 | 14.00 | 20.0 |
| 03.00 | 14.5 | 15.00 | 21.0 |
| 04.00 | 15.5 | 16.00 | 23.0 |
| 05.00 | 15.5 | 17.00 | 24.5 |
| 06.00 | 16.0 | 18.00 | 25.5 |
| 07.00 | 16.0 | 19.00 | 25.0 |
| 08.00 | 16.5 | 20.00 | 24.0 |
| 09.00 | 17.5 | 21.00 | 22.5 |
| 10.00 | 17.5 | 22.00 | 19.0 |
| 11.00 | 18.0 | 23.00 | 16.5 |

Reading from tables reliably is an important skill in science, as data are so often presented in tables. This is because tables allow data to be displayed in a systematic (and usually space-saving) way that allows a reader to make sense of the information quickly and easily. Look at Table 3.1. What are the maximum and minimum temperatures in the 24-hour period shown? Note these values down in the margin next to the table.

If you wrote the maximum and minimum temperatures as 25.5 and 14.5, you would not be completely correct. However, if you wrote 25.5 °C and 14.5 °C, you *would* have a full answer. The difference is that without the units, a value is meaningless, and you should *always* quote any units associated with a value. (The general use of units was revised in Box 2.1.)

The maximum and minimum temperatures are the most extreme values; if you had to summarise the overall behaviour with a single temperature value, it would be reasonable to calculate the mean of these two values. Remember this is calculated from the sum of the measurements divided by the number of measurements. Therefore, the mean of the two extreme temperatures is:

$$\frac{25.5\,°C + 14.5\,°C}{2} = \frac{40.0\,°C}{2} = 20.0\,°C$$

What is the mean of *all* the temperature measurements in Table 3.1? Again, it is the sum of the measurements divided by the number of measurements; this is the **mean surface temperature** for that day. The first step in calculating the mean temperature is to add together all the temperature values in Table 3.1. If you have a calculator handy, do this now. You should get 453.5 °C. The second step is to count the number of measurements, i.e. 24. Thus the mean surface temperature is given by 453.5 °C divided by 24. If you do this sum on your calculator, you will probably get a result displayed as 18.89583333 (indeed, your calculator may display even more digits).

The answer of 18.895 833 33 °C contains many decimal places (the .895 833 33 part of the number), but not all of these digits can be significant, given that the original temperature readings are recorded to only one decimal place. You cannot be certain about the digit that represents thousandths of a degree, let alone the digit that represents millionths of a degree. Scientists have conventions for the number of digits that they quote when writing a value, which is generally governed by considering the *level of uncertainty* they have about the value. If you understand how uncertain a number is, you can decide how many digits are appropriate. As this is an important concept, the next two sections look at it in detail.

## 3.1.2   Uncertainties

All the temperature measurements in Table 3.1 are recorded to one decimal place. But what determines the number of digits we should record when making measurements such as this? Why, for example, is the first temperature recorded as 16.0 °C, rather than 16 °C or 16.05 °C?

Figure 3.2 shows representations of two thermometers that are measuring the same air temperature. Thermometer A is indicating that the temperature is between 16 °C and 17 °C, so it is 'sixteen point something' °C. The 'something' cannot be read precisely – but it is a little less than half-way between the divisions corresponding to 16 °C and 17 °C, so the temperature could be estimated as 16.4 °C. You cannot be very confident about the value of this last digit; some people might record the temperature as 16.3 °C and others as 16.5 °C. Because of the uncertainty about the digit in the first decimal place, there is clearly no point in trying to guess a second decimal place here.

Now look at thermometer B in Figure 3.2, which has scale divisions every 0.1 °C.

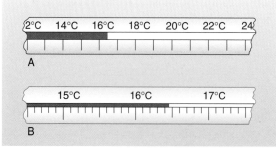

**Figure 3.2** Two thermometers, A and B, measuring the air temperature in the same place. Thermometer A has scale divisions of 1 °C whereas thermometer B has scale divisions of 0.1 °C.

■ What is the temperature indicated by thermometer B?

□ The temperature is between 16.4 °C and 16.5 °C. The second decimal place is rather uncertain, but it appears to be about 6, so you might record the temperature as 16.46 °C. However, you might think that the last digit should be 5 or 7.

To indicate how precisely the value from the thermometer can be read, an estimated uncertainty in the reading can be quoted. For the temperature measured by thermometer A, the displayed temperature is estimated to be within 0.1 °C of 16.4 °C, i.e. the displayed temperature could be as low as (16.4 − 0.1) °C or as high as (16.4 + 0.1) °C. This is quoted as 16.4 ± 0.1 °C, which is spoken as 'sixteen point four plus or minus zero point one degrees Celsius'. The temperature measured by thermometer B would probably be quoted as 16.46 ± 0.01 °C. The ± quantity (±0.1 °C in the first case and ±0.01 °C in the second) is usually referred to as the **uncertainty** in the measurement. You would say that the first measurement of 16.4 °C has an uncertainty associated with it of ±0.1 °C, and the second measurement of 16.46 °C has an uncertainty of ±0.01 °C.

However, this is not the end of the matter. When reading from a scale on a piece of experimental equipment – in this case a thermometer – can you *really* be confident that your measurement has an uncertainty of (e.g. in the case of thermometer A) ±0.1 °C when the manufacturer has given scale divisions of only 1 °C? Usually, the size of the scale divisions on a piece of equipment gives an approximate indication of the level of accuracy that the manufacturer believes the equipment can give. Thus, it is somewhat dangerous to assume that your uncertainty is much smaller than the size of one division on the scale. For this reason, it is safest to take a rather more conservative approach in recording measurements, and you should adopt the following convention.

It is the convention to record a reading from experimental equipment to the nearest half a division, and to quote the uncertainty of that reading as a value equal to half a division.

Thus, following this convention, you would record the reading from thermometer A (Figure 3.2) as 16.5 ± 0.5 °C, and the reading from thermometer B as 16.45 ± 0.05 °C.

Look again at the temperatures recorded in Table 3.1. The thermometer used probably had divisions of 1 °C, so the temperatures were recorded to the nearest 0.5 °C.

Important text is highlighted to indicate it is a key point to understand and memorise.

■ Although it is not given in Table 3.1, what do you think is the uncertainty associated with each temperature measurement?

☐ As the temperatures were recorded to the nearest 0.5 °C, the uncertainty would be ±0.5 °C.

### 3.1.3  Different types of uncertainty

The thermometers in Figure 3.2 illustrate the fact that there are uncertainties associated with taking a reading from experimental equipment. This is called **experimental uncertainty** as it comes about from uncertainties derived from the equipment or method being used to make the measurement. However, there are other types of uncertainty in measurements that may need considering too. Perhaps the air temperature fluctuates on a fairly short timescale because of variations in the wind and cloud cover, so that a series of measurements over two minutes shows a range of values. In this case, you could quantify the uncertainty in the actual air temperature by quoting the range of values. This type of uncertainty is an example of a **random uncertainty**, so called because the measured values are scattered fairly *randomly* about some mean value. Various effects that give rise to some fluctuations in a measurement value may be present (e.g. in the case of a temperature measurement, the wind, sunlight, cloud and rain may vary and affect the measurement); however, all these effects will combine to give one overall random uncertainty in the measurement. The random uncertainty associated with a given measurement can be estimated by repeating the measurement a number of times; the spread of the results indicates the random uncertainty that is present.

Measurements that have a small experimental uncertainty are said to be precise or of high precision. Another way of expressing this is to say that if the experimental uncertainty in a measurement is reduced (e.g. by using a better measuring instrument), the measurement can be more precise. Thus the temperature measured by thermometer B (in Figure 3.2) is more precise than the temperature measured by thermometer A. The experimental uncertainty and random uncertainty associated with a measurement may differ considerably. For example, you might take individual temperature readings to a precision (experimental uncertainty) of ±0.1 °C, but find when you repeat the measurement several times that the measured temperature can vary by much more – perhaps ±2 °C. That is, the random uncertainty associated with the determination of the *actual* temperature is ±2 °C, even though each individual measurement has a precision of ±0.1 °C.

When we want to indicate the actual spread in values when trying to determine a typical measurement, it is appropriate to quote the random uncertainty. However, when there is a lot of data, and you want to present a mean value and indicate the uncertainty in this mean value, an often-followed convention is to assume the uncertainty in the mean is the same as the experimental uncertainty of an individual measurement. To illustrate this, consider again the temperature data for a summer's day in Milton Keynes in Table 3.1. The mean was calculated (by a calculator) as 18.895 833 33 °C. As each individual measurement had a precision of $\pm 0.5$ °C (i.e. the experimental uncertainty was $\pm 0.5$ °C), it is appropriate to use the same value for the uncertainty in the mean. (There is a formal mathematical definition of the uncertainty in the mean, but it is beyond the scope of this course, so you should follow this assumption.) Thus the mean could be written as $18.895\,833\,33 \pm 0.5$ °C. However, as the uncertainty is to one decimal place, it is pointless using more than one decimal place for the mean also. So, in this case, the mean would be quoted as $18.9 \pm 0.5$ °C. Note that in turning the value $18.895\,833\,33$, which uses eight decimal places, into a value that uses just one decimal place, the value was rounded (in this case, rounded up). If you need a reminder about rounding decimal values, read Box 3.1 now.

## Box 3.1  Rounding decimal places

Everyone uses decimal numbers, based on the system of counting which is 'base 10' (i.e. multiples of 10). When using numbers smaller than one, the decimal places represent fractions of one: for example, 0.1 is a $\frac{1}{10}$ th, 0.01 is a $\frac{1}{100}$ th, 0.001 is a $\frac{1}{1000}$ th. Normally, you don't even think about it: you just write down a decimal number (e.g. the price is 7.99 euro). When doing a calculation, your calculator will often give an answer with as many digits as the display can handle.

■  Using a calculator, what is 7 divided by 50.37?

☐  According to a calculator, the answer is 0.138 971 611.

If it is inappropriate to quote all these decimal places, you need to round to fewer decimal places. Rounding is the process of writing an approximation of the actual number using fewer digits. For example, if you want to round 0.138 971 611 to two decimal places, you should not write 0.13. You need to consider what the first three decimal places are, i.e. one *more* than the number of places wanted. So, in this case, you have 0.138, which is closer to 0.14 than it is to 0.13. Thus you quote your two decimal number approximation as 0.14. If the number had instead been 0.132, you would argue that 0.132 was closer to 0.13 than to 0.14, and would quote your final number as 0.13. In essence, you are simply looking at the digit in the third decimal place, and deciding whether it is closer to 0 or 10. So, in the first case of 0.138, the third digit (8) is closer to 10, so you round the digit *up* from 8 to 10, which forces the digit in the second decimal place to become a 4

(i.e. you are adding one to this digit). In the second case of 0.132, the third digit (2) is closer to 0, so you round the digit *down* from 2 to 0, so the digit in the second decimal place is unaffected and stays as 3. You need to remember that the digit 5 gets rounded *up*, not down. So, 0.135 is 0.14 to two decimal places, whereas 0.134 is 0.13 to two decimal places.

Once you've done rounding a few times, it is straightforward. There are two pitfalls worth mentioning however. If you were asked to round 0.374 999 to two decimal places, the answer would be 0.37. Do not be tempted to round twice, i.e. first rounding to 0.375, and then rounding to 0.38. Furthermore, sometimes people are confused if rounding causes a 'chain reaction' in other digits. For example, if you want to quote 0.899 996 to five decimal places, you look at the sixth digit (i.e. 6), and decide you must round up; so you add one to the fifth digit. However, as the fifth digit is 9, adding one to it turns it to 10, which means you have to add one to the fourth digit, and so on. So, 0.899 996 to five decimal places becomes 0.900 00.

Do the following question to make sure you understand rounding of decimal places.

### Question 3.1

Round the following numbers:

(a)  12.345 6789 to one decimal place

(b)  12.345 6789 to two decimal places

(c)  3.141 5926 to three decimal places

(d)  0.900 999 to four decimal places

(e)  0.999 999 to one decimal place

There is one more type of uncertainty you should be aware of. It is another type of experimental uncertainty, and can be difficult to assess. It can be illustrated with the thermometer example again. You might be happily reading temperature from a scale with a precision of ±0.5 °C but what if the thermometer manufacturer had printed the scale on the outside of the thermometer slightly in the wrong place such that *every* reading you took was 1.5 °C lower than the true value? Your recorded values might apparently be precise to ±0.5 °C but every reading would actually be 1.5 °C too low. This means that (unknown to you) there is an error associated with every measurement. This is called a **systematic error**. If you subsequently discovered what the error was (i.e. each reading was 1.5 °C too low) then it would be easy to correct by systematically adding 1.5 °C to every value you recorded. Of course, you would probably never realise that the systematic error was there – all you might be able to say is that there is probably some **systematic uncertainty** associated with your readings, but you don't know how big this uncertainty is.

This highlights the difference between precision and accuracy. You might be able to make a measurement to a high precision: for example, you might be able to measure the *change* in temperature between two times very precisely. However, that does not necessarily mean that the individual values of temperature you recorded were accurate (i.e. were the true values) because there may be a systematic error that you don't know about.

The difference between random and systematic uncertainty is illustrated in Figure 3.3. Random uncertainties lead to a random distribution of the measured values around a 'true' value, and large and small random uncertainties are shown in Figure 3a and 3b respectively. A systematic error leads to an offset of the measured values from the 'true' value, as shown in Figure 3.3c.

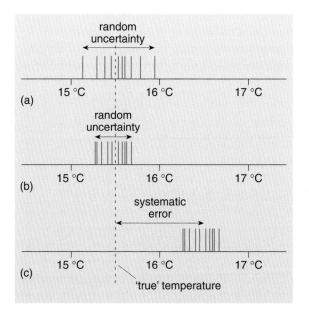

(a)

(b)

(c)

**Figure 3.3**   Measured values of temperature are indicated by the positions of the solid vertical lines on the temperature scales. (a) Large random uncertainties mean that individual measurements are randomly scattered in a large range about some 'true' value (indicated by the dashed vertical line). (b) Smaller random uncertainties lead to a smaller spread of individual measurements, but still clustered around the 'true' value. (c) A systematic error combined with a small random uncertainty leads to the group of measurements being displaced from the 'true' value.

### 3.1.4    Significant figures

You have seen that, when quoting a value for a measured quantity, you should not give more digits than you can justify in terms of the uncertainties in the measurements. Thus when you calculated the mean temperature as 18.895 8333 ± 0.5 °C, you rounded the value to one decimal place, giving 18.9 ± 0.5 °C. The smaller the uncertainties in the measurements, the greater will be the number of digits that can be quoted. The number of digits that you quote when you write down the value of a quantity is known as the number of **significant figures**. You would say that a value of 16.4 °C is quoted to three significant figures (which is often abbreviated to 'sig figs'), whereas the value 16.47 °C is quoted to four significant figures. In general, the last digit will be somewhat uncertain, but you will be confident about the other digits. Thus one possible definition of the number of 'significant' figures to use is the number of digits that you are certain of, plus one more (less certain) digit.

■ How many significant figures are quoted in the following temperatures: 1345 °C, 13.45 °C, 1.345 °C and 1.3 °C?

□ The first three temperatures are quoted to four significant figures, but there are only two significant figures in 1.3 °C.

Specifying the number of significant figures when zeros are involved can be a little trickier, as the following examples indicate.

- 0.082 m: there are only two significant figures here because initial zeros do not count. These initial zeros only tell you about the size of the number, and not about the precision to which it is known. The first significant figure in this value is 8.

- 50.6 m: there are three significant figures here, since the zero in the middle of a number counts as a significant figure in the same way as the other digits.

- 79.0 m: there are three significant figures here too. A zero at the end of a number and after the decimal point has the same significance as any other digit; if this value was known to only two significant figures, it would be quoted as 79 m.

- 900 m: this is the really tricky one. It could be that the value is known to one, two or three significant figures. The way around this ambiguity is to state explicitly the number of significant figures meant: for example, write '900 m (2 significant figures)'.

■ To how many significant figures are each of the following measurements given: (a) 1.240 mm; (b) 0.019 mm; (c) 10.0095 mm?

□ (a) Four significant figures; (b) two significant figures; (c) six significant figures.

Often, the issue of significant figures is best handled by writing values in scientific notation. For example, you saw that there was an ambiguity in the value 900 m (i.e. it could be one, two or three significant figures). This ambiguity would be avoided if the value was written in scientific notation, as the convention is to quote only the figures that are significant. (If you need a reminder about what scientific notation is, or are not confident that you can type such a number into a calculator, read Box 3.2 now.) So, 900 m (one significant figure) would be written $9 \times 10^2$ m; 900 m (two significant figures) would be written $9.0 \times 10^2$ m; and 900 m (three significant figures) would be written $9.00 \times 10^2$ m.

■ To how many significant figures are each of the following measurements given: (a) $6.4 \times 10^2$ m; (b) $5.405 \times 10^2$ m; (c) $5.405\ 00 \times 10^2$ m?

☐ (a) Two significant figures; (b) four significant figures; (c) six significant figures.

---

### Box 3.2   Scientific notation and its use with a calculator

**Scientific notation** is a useful way of writing numbers, particularly very large or very small numbers. Scientific notation relies on the fact that *any* value can be rewritten as a number that is *equal to or greater than 1 but less than 10*, multiplied by a simple power of ten. Take, for example, a number such as 123. In scientific notation this becomes $1.23 \times 10^2$. Similarly, 12 345 in scientific notation becomes $1.2345 \times 10^4$. In these two examples, the powers of ten are $10^2$ (i.e. 100) and $10^4$ (i.e. 10 000). When converting values that are less than one into scientific notation, the power of ten becomes negative. For example, 0.000 123 45 is $1.2345 \times 10^{-4}$ in scientific notation. This is because 0.000 123 45 is equal to $1.2345 \times 0.0001$ and

$$0.0001 = \frac{1}{10\ 000} = \frac{1}{10^4} = 10^{-4}$$

Note that 1 and 10 can also be written as powers of ten. You know that 100 is $10^2$ and 0.1 is $10^{-1}$; perhaps you can see that the 'in between' powers of ten are thus: $10 = 10^1$ and $1 = 10^0$. So, in scientific notation, 12.3 is $1.23 \times 10^1$ and 1.23 is $1.23 \times 10^0$. Note that any number written using a power of ten could be referred to as being in 'powers of ten' notation. Hence, $23.4 \times 10^4$ is in powers of ten

notation; however, it is only when written as $2.34 \times 10^5$ that it would be in proper scientific notation.

You should ensure that you can type numbers in scientific notation into your calculator correctly. For example, you should know the difference in entering, say, $-6.78 \times 10^6$ as opposed to $6.78 \times 10^{-6}$ (or indeed, $-6.78 \times 10^{-6}$). Also, do not fall into the trap of entering a simple power of ten, such as $10^4$, as $10 \times 10^4$ (which is actually $10^5$). This is avoided if you remember that $10^4$ is actually $1 \times 10^4$ in scientific notation. Finally, take care not to enter (or write), say, $3.46 \times 10^4$ as $3.46^4$.

Ensure you are comfortable with entering scientific notation and powers of ten into your calculator by checking you get the following answers to these multiplications and divisions.

$2.45 \times 10^5 \times 3.2 \times 10^7 = 7.84 \times 10^{12}$

$3 \times 10^8 \times 6.6 \times 10^{-34} = 1.98 \times 10^{-25}$

$6.666 \times 10^{-34} \div 2.222 \times 10^0 = 3 \times 10^{-34}$

$-2.1 \times 10^4 \times 2.1 \times 10^{-4} = -4.41$ (i.e. $-4.41 \times 10^0$)

$10^6 \times 10^6 = 10^{12}$ (i.e. $1 \times 10^{12}$)

$10^8 \div 10^{-34} = 10^{42}$ (i.e. $1 \times 10^{42}$)

$10^4 \times 3.14 = 31\ 400$ or $3.14 \times 10^4$

---

Of course, the results of measurements are often used in calculations, and you then need to know how many figures to quote in the answer (particularly as a calculator may display many digits). For example, imagine you want to calculate the area of a floor in a house, and you are given the measurements 3.9 m by 4.85 m. The floor area is 3.9 m $\times$ 4.85 m = 18.915 m$^2$. So the answer has five significant figures. Is this precision justified?

Two basic 'rules of thumb' are used to determine the number of digits quoted in an answer. Both are only guides but they reflect the basic concept behind all of this discussion, i.e. decide what the uncertainties related with the values in the calculation are, and then don't quote the answer to any more digits than these uncertainties justify. The rules are as follows.

> When multiplying and dividing numbers, the number of significant figures in the answer should be the same as the number of significant figures of the *least* precise value in the calculation.

This is similar to the concept of a chain only being as strong as its weakest link. An answer is only as precise as the least precise value in the calculation. For example, in the calculation above, the least precise value is 3.9 m, which has two significant figures. Thus the answer does not justify any more than two significant figures, and should be quoted as 19 m$^2$.

■ To how many significant figures should the answer to each of the following calculations be given: (a) $6.4 \times 5.23$; (b) $5.40 \times 3.345$; (c) $5.405 \div 0.1$; (d) $2.34 \times 10^5 \times 6.7 \times 10^3$.

☐ (a) Two significant figures; (b) three significant figures; (c) one significant figure; (d) two significant figures.

You should note that essentially the rule is simply saying that you identify the value that has the lowest number of significant figures, and use that to define the number of significant figures to use in the answer. However, there is one situation that can catch people out. That is when calculations have exact multiples in them. For example, if the length of a piece of string is 111 mm, how long would a piece of string be that was *exactly* double this length. Clearly, you can immediately see the answer is 222 mm. However, formally, you did a calculation in your head which was $2 \times 111$ mm and, if you simply look for the value with the lowest number of significant figures (i.e. the 2), you might conclude that the answer merits only one significant figure (which would be 200 mm to one significant figure). In fact, the 2 represents a precise value. It is an **integer** – an *exact* whole number. It is not 'about 2' or 2.0 or 1.999 9999; it is *exactly* 2. In this respect, an integer is the *most* precise type of number you can imagine. Thus in your simple calculation, the 2 is absolutely precise and the 111 mm is the least precise term. Thus the answer should be quoted to three significant figures, i.e. 222 mm, which is the expected answer.

> When adding and subtracting numbers, think in terms of decimal places rather than in terms of significant figures. Again, identify the least precise value in the calculation and use the same precision in the answer. Thus the number of decimal places in the answer should be the same as in the value with the smallest number of decimal places in the calculation.

Note that this rule assumes that either the numbers are not written in powers of ten notation, or the numbers all involve the *same* power of ten. For example, if the mass of a bag of potatoes was measured as 12.8 kg, and you added to it a potato with a mass of 0.33 kg, the calculated value of the total mass would be 13.13 kg. However, since the first mass was measured to only one decimal place (i.e. it is the least precise measurement), you are justified in quoting the total mass to only one decimal place, so you would quote the answer as 13.1 kg (which happens to be three significant figures). Similarly, if the mass of the bag of potatoes was measured as 13 kg, and you added to it the potato with a mass of 0.33 kg, the answer should be quoted as 13 kg, because the input value (13 kg) has zero decimal places and thus the answer should also be limited to zero decimal places, and hence is also 13 kg. This might seem a little strange but it merely reflects that the initial value was precise only to the nearest kilogram, so you can't be more precise than that in the answer.

### Question 3.2

Do the following calculations and express your answers to the appropriate number of significant figures.

(a)  $0.43 + 1.217$

(b)  $8.1 - 3.82$

(c)  $2.373 \times 3.6$

(d)  $6342 \div 2.42$

(e)  $1111.1 \times 10^4 + 1.1111 \times 10^4$

The idea of significant figures in the context of measurements was introduced so that the link with the precision, accuracy and uncertainties in measurements could be emphasised. Almost all of the numbers quoted in this course will be measured values of some quantity or another, and the number of significant figures quoted will indicate the uncertainty in the value. When doing calculations with these values, you will need to bear in mind the two rules outlined above for deciding how many significant figures (or decimal places) should be quoted in the answer.

## 3.1.5  Measuring temperature revisited

Before this rather long, but important, interlude about uncertainties and significant figures, you were considering the mean surface temperature in Milton Keynes on a summer's day. From data in Table 3.1 you found that the mean temperature would be quoted as $18.9 \pm 0.5\ °C$.

Just as this mean surface temperature for one day was calculated, an **annual mean surface temperature** can be calculated using measurements taken at frequent and regular intervals throughout a year. The procedure for calculating the annual mean surface temperature can be written as:

$$\text{annual mean surface temperature} = \frac{\text{sum of all temperatures during the year}}{\text{number of measurements}} \quad (3.1)$$

Equations will often be numbered so that they can be referred to later.

Of course, no two years are identical because there will be either an unusually cold or an unusually warm year every now and then. To avoid the effects of an unusual year, and to serve as a benchmark against which to judge annual mean temperatures, meteorologists have adopted a convention of calculating a **30-year mean surface temperature**, which is calculated as follows.

1    The surface temperature is recorded several times a day, every day for a period of 30 years.

2    The 30-year mean surface temperature is then calculated by adding up all the temperature values, and dividing the sum by the total number of values.

Calculating a 30-year mean surface temperature smoothes out the variability of the weather at a particular location, and avoids being overly influenced by unusual individual extreme temperatures: for example, the UK's most extreme temperatures (at the time of writing) were 38.5 °C, recorded at Brogdale in Kent on 10 August 2003, and −26.1 °C recorded at Newport in Shropshire on 10 January 1982. However, the quest in this book is to understand what determines the *mean* temperature, and not the short-term variations above and below it. Moreover, this book is about the Earth as a whole – you need the global picture.

## 3.2    Global mean surface temperature

The primary concern here is with the mean surface temperature averaged over the whole surface of the Earth, both land and sea – the **global mean surface temperature (GMST)**. Usually the average is taken over one or more years. This means obtaining the mean surface temperature at very many locations around the globe, and working out their mean value, as follows.

$$\text{GMST} = \frac{\text{sum of all mean surface temperatures}}{\text{number of surface locations}} \tag{3.2}$$

This is illustrated for a more restricted region in Question 3.3.

Question 3.3

(a)    Calculate the UK's 30-year mean surface temperature from the data given in Figure 3.4.

(b)    What would need to be done to obtain a more representative value?

The value for the UK's 30-year mean surface temperature that you calculated in Question 3.3 (based on the data in Figure 3.4) is not very accurate. This is because the locations shown in Figure 3.4 do not give an even coverage of the UK – most of the locations are in the south or on the coast. A more representative value is 9.2 °C, obtained from 25 weather stations distributed more evenly around the country. Indeed, for calculating the GMST, it is desirable to spread weather stations uniformly over the globe. In practice, however, the spread is not uniform, weather stations being scarce in remote cold polar regions and over the oceans. To avoid the GMST being biased towards values from densely monitored areas, a mean temperature is calculated for each region of the Earth and these mean values are combined into a single GMST.

Whatever the method, finding the GMST involves a huge international effort requiring literally millions of measurements, all carefully taken, documented and assessed for accuracy. Various effects that might bias measurements are taken into account. For example, measurements taken in or near urban areas can

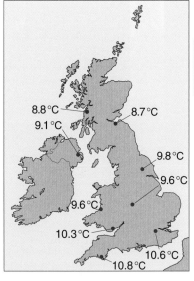

**Figure 3.4**   The British Isles with the 30-year mean surface temperature (from data obtained between 1961 and 1990) indicated for a number of locations in the UK.

sometimes give local temperatures significantly higher than would be recorded in a nearby rural area. This is because over large urban regions the air temperature is raised by human activity – building heating systems, vehicles, electrical appliances, and the huge number of people – and because construction materials (concrete, metal, glass, etc.) help to store heat accumulated in the day. Thus the air directly over a city can have a noticeably higher temperature than the surrounding land. This is known as an urban heat island. To give you an idea of how large this effect can be, Table 3.2 lists four examples.

**Table 3.2** Maximum urban heat island temperature increase for four European cities of different sizes.

| City | Population at time of temperature measurements | Maximum urban heat island temperature increase/°C* |
|---|---|---|
| Lund, Sweden | 50 000 | 5.8 |
| Malmo, Sweden | 275 000 | 7.4 |
| Vienna, Austria | 1870 000 | 8.0 |
| London, UK | 8500 000 | 10.0 |

\* Typically the effect is not as large as this – these values are the most extreme that will be encountered.

If the GMST corresponds to 30 consecutive years of averaging then it is called the 30-year GMST. Table 3.3 summarises the naming convention for all the different mean temperatures. *Changes* in the GMST can be measured quite accurately, and the data show that for the period 1971 to 2000, the 30-year GMST was 0.1 °C higher than the period 1961 to 1990. This indicates that in ten years, the 30-year GMST has risen by about 0.1 °C. Is a rise of 0.1 °C over 10 years unusual? Or is this small variation typical for this sort of data? To answer these questions requires a consideration of the history of variation in annual GMST values.

**Table 3.3** The naming convention for the various mean temperatures.

| Name | Meaning |
|---|---|
| mean surface temperature | the surface temperature at some location or over some region, averaged over some (unspecified) timespan |
| annual mean surface temperature | the surface temperature at some location or over some region, averaged over a year |
| 30-year mean surface temperature | the surface temperature at some location or over some region, averaged over 30 consecutive years |
| global mean surface temperature (GMST) | the mean surface temperature averaged over the whole globe, usually over one or more years |
| 30-year global mean surface temperature (30-year GMST) | the mean surface temperature averaged over the whole globe, over 30 consecutive years |

## 3.3 GMST in the recent past

It was not until the 17th century that the invention of the thermometer allowed reasonably reliable records of temperature to be compiled. In this section you will look at data from one area over relatively recent history, and then consider what can be deduced about prehistoric values of temperature.

### 3.3.1 The temperature record of central England

There is a remarkable temperature record that extends back to January 1659 for lowland areas of central England. The English meteorologist Gordon Manley (1902–1980) painstakingly collated and interpreted many thermometer readings and general diary entries on weather conditions (see, for example, Figure 3.5), to produce monthly mean temperatures for a representative site. The oldest records he had to deal with comprised diverse readings from different places, taken over different periods of time, using thermometers of varying accuracy, placed in different sites (shade, indoors, outdoors) and read at different times of day. Standardising the data to produce values that can be considered representative and comparable from year to year took very careful assessment. Some measurements had to be discarded as unreliable. The documents describing

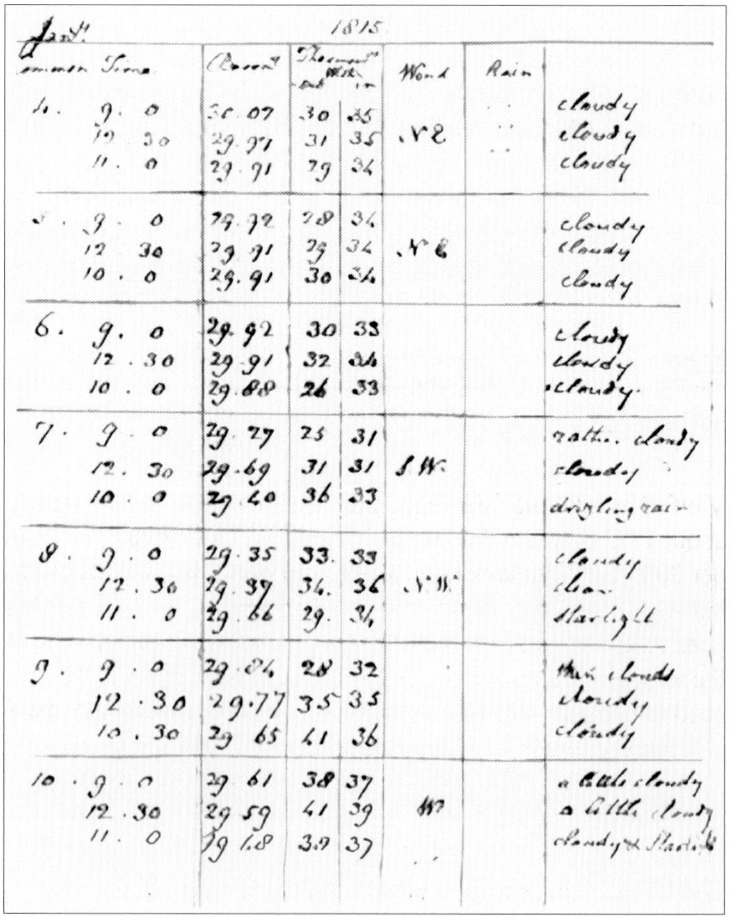
1815

| Jan.y | Time | Barom.r | Thermom.r With. | In | Wind | Rain | |
|---|---|---|---|---|---|---|---|
| 4. | 9. 0 | 30.07 | 30 | 35 | | | cloudy |
| | 12. 30 | 29.97 | 31 | 35 | NE | | cloudy |
| | 11. 0 | 29.91 | 29 | 34 | | | cloudy |
| 5. | 9. 0 | 29.92 | 28 | 34 | | | cloudy |
| | 12. 30 | 29.91 | 29 | 34 | NE | | cloudy |
| | 10. 0 | 29.91 | 30 | 34 | | | cloudy |
| 6. | 9. 0 | 29.92 | 30 | 33 | | | cloudy |
| | 12. 30 | 29.91 | 32 | 34 | | | cloudy |
| | 10. 0 | 29.88 | 26 | 33 | | | cloudy. |
| 7. | 9. 0 | 29.77 | 25 | 31 | | | rather cloudy |
| | 12. 30 | 29.69 | 31 | 31 | SW | | cloudy |
| | 10. 0 | 29.40 | 36 | 33 | | | drizzling rain |
| 8. | 9. 0 | 29.35 | 33. | 33 | | | cloudy |
| | 12. 30 | 29.39 | 34. | 36 | NW | | clear |
| | 11. 0 | 29.66 | 29. | 34 | | | starlight |
| 9. | 9. 0 | 29.84 | 28 | 32 | | | thin clouds |
| | 12. 30 | 29.77 | 35 | 35 | | | cloudy |
| | 10. 30 | 29.65 | 41 | 36 | | | cloudy |
| 10. | 9. 0 | 29.61 | 38 | 37 | | | a little cloudy |
| | 12. 30 | 29.59 | 41 | 39 | W | | a little cloudy |
| | 11. 0 | 29.68 | 39 | 37 | | | cloudy & starlight |

**Figure 3.5** A page of temperature values (in degrees Fahrenheit) and other weather observations taken three times daily from 4 to 10 January 1815, at the Radcliffe Observatory in Oxford. The outdoor and indoor temperatures are listed in the third and fourth columns respectively.

conditions before 1720 are sometimes sketchy, so Manley could estimate mean temperatures for each month only to the nearest degree Celsius. The more reliable data for later years are thought to be good to the nearest 0.2 °C. Daily temperatures representative of central England are available from 1772 onwards.

So what does the temperature record of central England reveal? Figure 3.6 is a graph of the annual mean surface temperature for every year between 1659 and 2006. It does not show individual data points (which vary considerably) but shows the overall trend of the data (so 'smoothing' out variations over short timescales). In fact, the overall mean temperature over the whole period is 9.2 °C, which is drawn as a horizontal line on the graph. You should be able to recognise that:

- the temperature data fluctuate considerably on a timescale of 10 to 25 years

- from the start of the record until about 1700, the data are mostly below 9.2 °C

- since about 1900, the data are mostly above 9.2 °C.

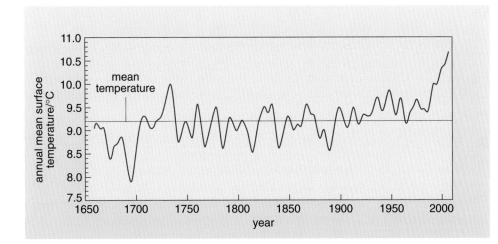

**Figure 3.6**  Trend of mean annual surface temperature for central England between 1659 and 2006. The mean temperature of 9.2 °C is indicated by a horizontal line.

Viewed as a whole, the temperature record of central England reveals warming of about 1 °C between the late 1600s and the late 1900s. The change of about 1 °C per 300 years amounts to an average of one-third of a degree Celsius per century, but with a period of rapid warming between 1690 and 1730 (where the graph rises steeply), and a period of more gradual warming since about 1900. Although the temperature record of central England is unaffected by urban heat islands, we need to consider whether the warming it shows is a purely local phenomenon or is it representative of an overall warming of the Earth's entire surface.

### 3.3.2  The recent historical record of GMST

The UK's Meteorological Office and the University of East Anglia produced sufficient data to make fairly confident conclusions about the change in annual

GMST for every year since 1850. Figure 3.7 shows the temperature *difference* between each yearly GMST and an adopted 'reference' temperature; this reference temperature is the 30-year mean value GMST for 1961–1990, and is *about* 15 °C. In this case, individual points are plotted but, as in Figure 3.6, a smoothed curve is shown to allow you to follow the overall trends. Concentrate for now on the individual data points in Figure 3.7.

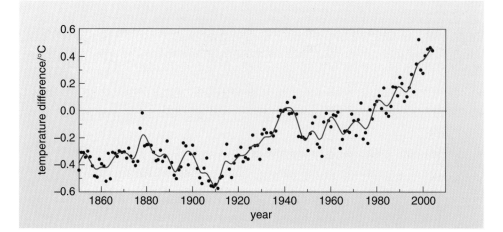

**Figure 3.7**   Difference in annual GMST from the 1961–1990 mean (of about 15 °C), showing the annual data between 1850 and 2004 and the smoothed trend.

■  What is the approximate difference in GMST between the first and last year?

☐  In 1850, the GMST was about 0.4 °C below the reference 30-year mean (1961–1990), whereas the 2004 value was about 0.4 °C higher than the reference value. The change from the 1850 value to the 2004 value therefore amounts to 0.4 °C − (−0.4 °C) = 0.8 °C, i.e. an increase of about 0.8 °C.

The most obvious features brought out by the smoothed curve in Figure 3.7 are two periods of sustained warming and two periods in which the GMST fluctuated without any overall warming or cooling trend. Deciding precisely when the fluctuations end and the warming begins is open to debate; however, the results show little evidence of a trend before 1900, marked warming to 1940, relatively steady conditions to the mid-1970s and a subsequent rapid warming. As you saw above, the smoothed curve indicates that the GMST increased by some 0.8 °C or so between 1850 and 2004.

■  What is the average rate of warming (in °C per century) between these dates?

☐  There are 154 years between 1850 and 2004, so a rise of 0.8 °C in 154 years is equivalent to $\dfrac{0.8\,°C}{154\ \text{years}}$ i.e. 0.0052 °C per year, or 0.5 °C per century (to 1 significant figure).

Although the trend is one of overall warming since 1850, the rate has not been constant. Also, although Figure 3.7 does not show it, the temperature change, and the rate of change, have not been the same everywhere on Earth. Near the Equator, the rate of warming has been less than 0.1 °C per century, whereas in the Arctic and Antarctic the rate is close to 1.5 °C per century. However, there is no question then that, in the past century, the Earth has been undergoing global warming. The reasons for this are less obvious, and whether the increase in GMST is unusual depends to some extent on whether the recent trend is the beginning of a real long-term increase in temperature or just a 'feature' in a series of erratic temperature changes. Might episodes of warming such as those happening now have been common over the last few million years? The answer to this question requires information about ancient temperatures, so curves such as in Figure 3.7 can be extended backwards over very long periods of time.

Before moving on to look at the distant past, you should update recent GMST values, in Activity 3.1.

---

## Activity 3.1    Updating the GMST data beyond 2004

We expect this activity will take you approximately 30 minutes.

The data shown in Figure 3.7 extend up to 2004. Clearly, it is important to continue to monitor GMST into the future. So, you should now retrieve more recent GMST data, from the course website, so you can update the GMST data set. (A data set refers to a collection of data.) Do this by carrying out the next two tasks.

Task 1    Obtaining more recent GMST data

Go to Activity 3.1 on the course website. This page will give you the most up-to-date data available.

Task 2    Adding the data to a plot of GMST

Figure 3.8 shows a subset of the data in Figure 3.7 (i.e. the most recent data for 1970–2004), plotted on standard graph paper, with the horizontal axis extending to 2020. As in Figure 3.7, the data shows the difference in annual GMST from the 30-year mean for 1961–1990. Plot points for the more recent data you obtained from the course website onto Figure 3.8. You now have an up-to-date record of the recent variation in GMST.

Question 3.4

From the up-to-date Figure 3.8 you have produced, is there any indication that the overall trend of increasing GMST is continuing beyond 2004, or is it too hard to tell because of random year-to-year variations?

There are no comments on this activity.

---

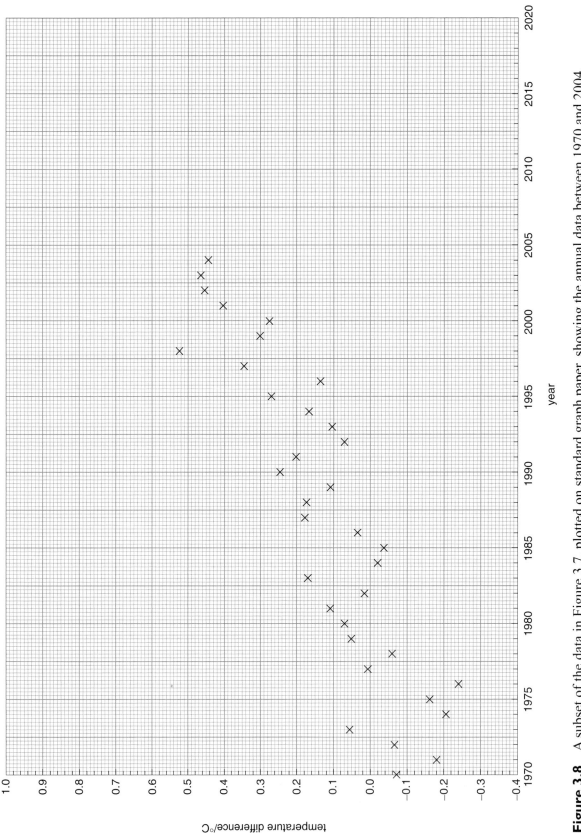
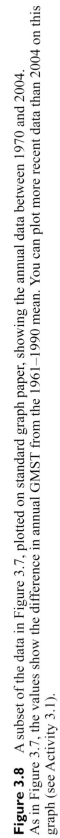

**Figure 3.8**  A subset of the data in Figure 3.7, plotted on standard graph paper, showing the annual data between 1970 and 2004. As in Figure 3.7, the values show the difference in annual GMST from the 1961–1990 mean. You can plot more recent data than 2004 on this graph (see Activity 3.1).

## 3.4    GMST in the distant past

You have seen that, in the last 100 years or so, there has undoubtedly been global warming. But is this unusual compared with what might have occurred in the distant past? Clearly, there is a need to find out what has happened thousands and even millions of years in the past to assess whether what is happening now is unusual.

### 3.4.1    Evidence from ancient organisms

(a)                                                                                            (b)

**Figure 3.9**    Photographs of an area of (a) rainforest and (b) Arctic tundra (a treeless region that has permanently frozen subsoil).

One of the best indicators of what the temperature of a region of the Earth was in the distant past is given by the vegetation that inhabited the region. Some plants thrive in hot and humid conditions (e.g. a rainforest; see Figure 3.9a) and some plants are suited to cold and icy conditions (e.g. the Arctic tundra; see Figure 3.9b). So there is a need to know what plants existed in various places at various times in the past. This information is obtained by investigating fossils. A **fossil** is evidence of any ancient animal or plant, usually preserved in stone but sometimes in other types of material, such as peat or amber. Figure 3.10 shows an example of a fossil tree. Although located in what is now a desert, it is fairly safe to assume that the climate must have been within the range of conditions under which trees live today. For example, while trees are found in many different local climates, they tend not to survive where the mean summer temperature is less than about 10 °C, or where there is an inadequate supply of water. Thus the fossilised trees in Figure 3.10 indicate that the local climate in which they existed, was neither very cold, nor very dry.

**Figure 3.10**    Fossil tree trunks in western China which were alive 150 million years ago; today the area is a desert but the climate was wetter when the trees were alive.

Large fossils such as the tree trunks in Figure 3.10 are quite rare; fossils of microscopic pollen grains are much more numerous. Many plants shed pollen from the male parts of their flowers, and the pollen is carried on the wind or by insects to the female parts of flowers where fertilisation occurs. This process is how the plants produce their seeds. The spring and summer air becomes heavily

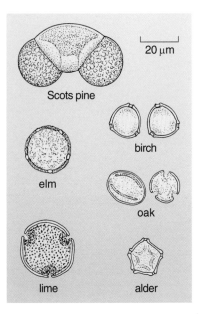

**Figure 3.11**    Drawings of various pollen grains from different types of tree. The scale bar represents 20 μm; pollen grains are typically between 10 μm and 50 μm across.

laden with pollen (as people who get hay fever know well) and a mature tree can produce many tens of millions of pollen grains each year. Most pollen grains never reach the flowers they were intended for, but instead fall to the ground or onto the surface of lakes and streams. Pollen grains can be deposited in the silt accumulating on the bottom of lakes or in peat accumulating in bogs and become preserved as fossils. Because plants produce huge numbers of pollen grains, just one spoonful of peat can contain many thousands of pollen grains from the trees, shrubs and grasses in the vicinity of the peat bog. Furthermore, because each type of plant produces pollen with a unique shape and surface pattern, it is possible to identify the range of plant types that have contributed to a given sample of pollen. Figure 3.11 shows drawings of various pollen grains. Note the scale bar indicating that these small pollen grains are only about 20 μm across. (If you need reminding of the μm unit, or indeed the use of prefixes for units in general, read Box 3.3 (opposite) now.)

Question 3.5

Figure 3.12 shows a photograph of pollen grains taken from a 140 000-year-old sample of Essex clay. Compare their shapes with those shown in the drawing of pollen grains in Figure 3.11. Can you identify any of the pollen grains? Do you think that the local trees included oak and Scots pine, or elm and lime?

**Figure 3.12**    Photograph of pollen grains that have been carefully separated and extracted from a sample of clay from Marks Tey, near Colchester, UK, magnified by a microscope.

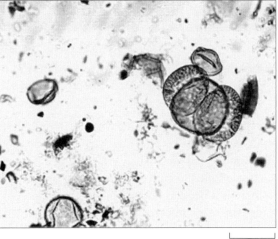

The usefulness of fossil pollen to the scientist is that the types and proportions of pollen in a sample, such as in Figure 3.12, can be compared with those produced by vegetation growing in present-day climates. The climate at the time the pollen was produced can then be inferred. This returns to the main thread of this section, which is the pattern of temperature change on the Earth through time.

By collecting a series of pollen samples of different ages from a given area or site, and inferring the climate that produced each sample, a picture of how climate (or just temperature) changed over time can be deduced. Samples of different ages are obtained by taking samples from different depths below the surface of a peat bog or lake bed. In the case of the peat bog, successive layers of organic matter grow and decay on the surface, progressively burying older

## Box 3.3  Using prefixes with units

So far, units such as metre and kilometre have been used without comment. Now is a good time to remind you of the use of prefixes. Consider the number next to the scale bar in Figure 3.11: 20 μm. The unit μm, or micrometre, is one-millionth of a metre, i.e. 1 μm = $1 \times 10^{-6}$ m. So, to convert μm into m, you multiply by $10^{-6}$. It is the prefix *micro* that tells you to use $10^{-6}$. Thus, 20 μm = $20 \times 10^{-6}$ m = $2.0 \times 10^{-5}$ m (in scientific notation). Other prefixes would indicate other multipliers. For example *kilo* indicates that you multiply by $10^{3}$ (hence 1 km = $1 \times 10^{3}$ m). Table 3.4 shows the most common prefixes used with SI units.

**Table 3.4**  Prefixes used with SI units. Note μ is the Greek letter 'mu'.

| Prefix | Symbol | Multiplying factor |
|--------|--------|--------------------|
| tera   | T      | $\times 10^{12}$   |
| giga   | G      | $\times 10^{9}$    |
| mega   | M      | $\times 10^{6}$    |
| kilo   | k      | $\times 10^{3}$    |
| –      | –      | $\times 10^{0} = 1$ |
| deci   | d      | $\times 10^{-1}$   |
| centi  | c      | $\times 10^{-2}$   |
| milli  | m      | $\times 10^{-3}$   |
| micro  | μ      | $\times 10^{-6}$   |
| nano   | n      | $\times 10^{-9}$   |
| pico   | p      | $\times 10^{-12}$  |
| femto  | f      | $\times 10^{-15}$  |
| atto   | a      | $\times 10^{-18}$  |

You can see from Table 3.4, for example, that 12 fm (femtometre) = $12 \times 10^{-15}$ m, or that 7 dm (decimetre) = $7 \times 10^{-1}$ m, or that 5 ns (nanosecond) = $5 \times 10^{-9}$ s. A slight confusion can arise because the SI unit of mass is the kilogram, symbol kg. So it seems reasonable to assume that 1000 kilograms would be written as 1 kilokilogram. However, it never is: it is kilogram, kg; gram, g ($10^{-3}$ kg); milligram, mg ($10^{-6}$ kg), etc. So the prefixes are applied as if the gram is the SI unit, even though it isn't. To complicate matters further, you often see 'tonne' used, where 1 tonne = $10^{3}$ kg, and then tonne being used with SI prefixes too.

■  How many kg are in 1 kt (kilotonne), 1 Mt (megatonne) and 1 Gt (gigatonne)?

☐  1 kt = $10^{3}$ tonne = $10^{6}$ kg; 1 Mt = $10^{6}$ tonne = $10^{9}$ kg; 1 Gt = $10^{9}$ tonne = $10^{12}$ kg.

Another pitfall that you should avoid is forgetting to use a space between separate units, so that it looks like you have used a prefix instead. For example, metres per second should be written m $s^{-1}$ (i.e. a space between m and $s^{-1}$), and not $ms^{-1}$, which would mean per millisecond.

It is worth mentioning one extra unit and use of prefixes here: time measured in years, which is usually abbreviated to the symbol y. So, you may often see $y^{-1}$ meaning per year. However, when dealing with geological time (i.e. long timespans that are often measured in millions of years), you would expect to use My, megayear ($\times 10^{6}$ y) or Gy, gigayear ($\times 10^{9}$ y). However, My and Gy units are usually written Ma and Ga, where the 'a' stands for *annum* (meaning year). You may also see $y^{-1}$ (per year) written as per annum, pa. So, the Earth is $4.6 \times 10^{9}$ y old, i.e. it is 4.6 Ga, or 4600 Ma old; alternatively, the Earth was formed 4600 Ma ago.

peat. Likewise on the lake bed, the most recently deposited silt covers previously deposited layers of silt. So, by boring down into the deposits a column, or core, of material can be extracted, which gives a layer-by-layer record of sedimentation and pollen accumulation over time (Figure 3.13, overleaf). The deeper the sample in the core, the older it will be. The age of a sample, in years, is worked out using specialist techniques, but it is the results rather than the dating techniques that are of interest here.

**Figure 3.13** (a) Scientists obtaining a core of sediment from the bed of Lake Igelsjoen, Sweden. (b) Part of the extracted core showing alternating dark and light layers of silt that were deposited 5000 years ago. The scale is marked in centimetres; the section of core visible is about 14 cm long.

(a)                          (b)

Evidence of changing climate is indicated by changes in the proportion of different pollen types throughout the core sample. A good example of these fossil pollen investigations is the data from the bed of a lake at Hockham Mere in Norfolk, UK. Rather than displaying the data as lists of numbers in a table, it is easier to see trends when the data are plotted as a graph. This is shown for the Hockham Mere data in Figure 3.14, for six different tree pollens. This sort of figure is called a **pollen diagram**. This way of plotting data is unusual, the vertical axis increasing in value down the page (the opposite of how graphs usually appear). However, this is useful as core samples are being considered which increase in depth as they go down into the ground.

Figure 3.14 shows some striking changes in the proportions of pollen types with depth (and hence time from the present day).

■ At a depth of about 7 m, what percentage of all the tree pollen in the samples is from birch?

☐ At 7 m depth, about 90% of all the tree pollen is birch.

So at greater depths, which happen to be for periods approaching 10 000 years ago, birch pollen was dominant. However, at shallower depths (i.e. more recent times), oak and alder dominate, with the proportion of birch (and Scots pine) decreasing. These changes were brought about by changes in the local climate over the last 10 000 years. In fact, there was a significant warming over this period, which favoured the growth of trees such as oak and alder.

To extend this sort of pollen diagram analysis further back in time simply requires core samples that penetrate into older layers (i.e. to a greater depth). One of the most remarkable core samples, providing a record over the past 140 000 years, is from Grande Pile in the Vosges region of eastern France.

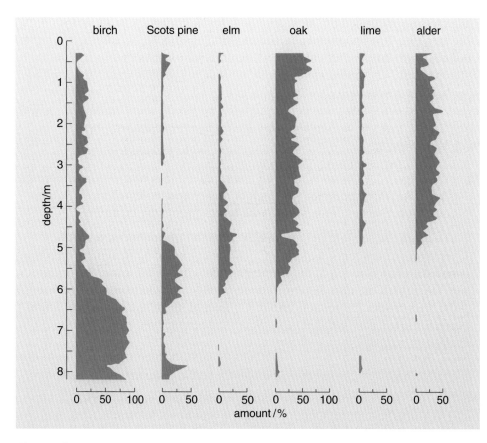

**Figure 3.14**   Tree pollen diagrams for birch, Scots pine, elm, oak, lime and alder, derived from a core sample taken from a lake bed in Hockham Mere. A depth of 8 m corresponds to approximately 10 000 years ago. The amounts are the percentage of all tree pollen in the sample.

Figure 3.15 shows a pollen diagram for this core, simplified to show the percentage of all the pollen present, that comes from trees. The difference between this, and 100%, represents the percentage of all pollen that comes from plants other than trees.

The method of assigning temperatures to each part of a pollen diagram is complex, but basically relies on making observations of present-day climates and flora (the mix of plant types present in an area) so that the temperature conditions required for particular sets of plants to thrive can be identified. The results can then be applied in reverse, starting with a mix of plants found in an ancient pollen sample (derived from pollen diagrams for many types of plant) and inferring the temperatures appropriate for those plants. Applying these techniques, the 140 000-year pollen record from Grande Pile has been converted into the 140 000-year record of long-term mean temperature shown in Figure 3.16. Note that the results are shown as a shaded band rather than a thin line. This is because there is considerable uncertainty in estimating an accurate temperature for each pollen sample, and so the result is expressed as falling within a likely range of temperatures (i.e. within the shaded region) rather than as a definite value.

Figure 3.16 is plotted in the same style as the pollen diagrams, i.e. with age increasing downwards. This convention conveys the idea that information about older times is more deeply buried in the original core. Note that the vertical axis is labelled 'age/10³ years'. This means that the numbers read from the vertical

**Figure 3.15**   Pollen diagram for the core from Grande Pile, France, showing the percentage of all pollen that comes from trees. The core depth extends to about 19 m, which corresponds to approximately 140 000 years ago.

47

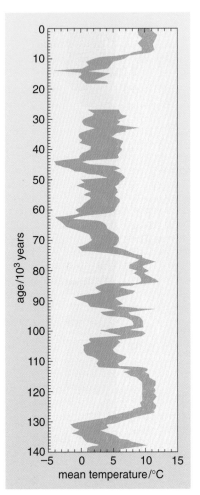

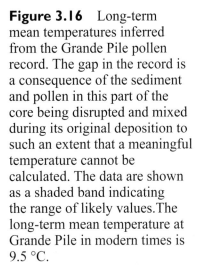

**Figure 3.16** Long-term mean temperatures inferred from the Grande Pile pollen record. The gap in the record is a consequence of the sediment and pollen in this part of the core being disrupted and mixed during its original deposition to such an extent that a meaningful temperature cannot be calculated. The data are shown as a shaded band indicating the range of likely values. The long-term mean temperature at Grande Pile in modern times is 9.5 °C.

scale must be multiplied by $10^3$ years: for example, 20 on the scale means $20 \times 10^3$ years. The horizontal axis shows that temperature increases to the right. Figure 3.16 reveals several cold periods separated by warmer periods, all of different durations. Temperatures during the warmer periods were similar to those of today. The colder periods were typically 6 to 10 °C colder. The transitions between cold and warm periods occurred over relatively short timespans – within about 10 000 years or so – and so these were periods of relatively rapid temperature change.

■ From Figure 3.16, what would you estimate the mean temperature is over the *whole* 140 000-year period (this will be a very approximate value)? Is this value higher, lower or the same as the recent mean temperature (9.5 °C)?

☐ The mean temperature over the whole 140 000-year period is probably somewhere between 3 °C and 5 °C. This is estimated by imagining a vertical line such that as much of the temperature data lies to the left of the line as to the right of the line. This overall mean value is considerably lower than the recent mean temperature of 9.5 °C. (Indeed, there have been only a few periods in the past 140 000 years where the climate has been as warm as it is in the present day.)

Put another way, you can see that although the recent temperatures are taken for granted, they are actually quite unusual with respect to the conditions over the past 140 000 years.

### 3.4.2    Evidence from the ancient past – ice ages

In the previous section you saw that past temperatures can be inferred from fossil pollens. The reconstructed temperature history of the Grande Pile region of France over the past 140 000 years (Figure 3.16) shows that between about 75 000 and 10 000 years ago the mean temperature was consistently lower than that of today. (Indeed, fossil evidence from many other places also indicates relatively cold conditions during the same interval.) This was a **glacial period**, when much of the UK, northern Eurasia and northern America were glaciated, i.e. the landscape was covered in ice and **glaciers** – 'rivers of ice' (Figure 3.17). In fact, there is evidence of relatively recent glaciation in landscape features that have been eroded by the passage of a glacier. U-shaped valleys (carved out by the passing glacier) and glacial till and moraines (mounds or sheets of boulders and rock fragments produced by the grinding action of the glacier) leave tell-tale signs that there has been glaciation in a region. However, it is less obvious from the landscape features *when* the glaciation took place.

Evidence from older fossils found elsewhere allows the Earth's temperature record to be extended further back in time. (It is also possible to use fossil insects, shellfish and microscopic marine plants and animals to calculate temperatures both on land and in the oceans.) This has revealed that in the last 2.4 million years (a period nearly 20 times longer than that covered by the Grande Pile record), there have been several glacial periods lasting for up to hundreds of thousands of years, separated by shorter **interglacial periods** with more temperate conditions. The total collection of glacial and interglacial periods constitutes an **ice age**. So, according to this pattern, the relatively warm

**Figure 3.17**  A glacier in Greenland. The frozen landscape of eastern Greenland is so cold that a permanent ice sheet is present, from which glaciers slowly spill out like a very slow-flowing river.

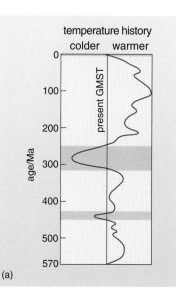

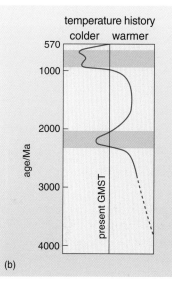

**Figure 3.18**  Generalised temperature history of Earth relative to the current GMST (the vertical line), but note that the temperature scale is qualitative. The times when major ice ages occurred are identified by the (blue) horizontal shaded bands. As in Figure 3.16, age increases downwards. (a) The last 570 Ma when the record is reasonably reliable. (b) The older record, with a compressed vertical scale extending back to the Earth's very early days.

conditions of today's climate are due to the fact that we are in an interglacial period that started about 10 000 years ago. This is part of an ice age that began some 2.4 million years ago (this may surprise you – we are currently in an ice age!). So, during an ice age the world is not permanently locked in the grip of ice sheets, but experiences periods of glaciation interspersed by more temperate conditions. Looking back at Figure 3.16, you can see that we are currently in an interglacial period, but it seems reasonable to expect that at some time in the (not too distant) future the present interglacial period will come to an end and be replaced by a glacial period. Indeed, a few decades ago, before the topic of global warming became more widely discussed, the media were more concerned with the idea that the world would soon be plunged back into a glacial period.

The Earth is about 4600 million years (i.e. 4600 Ma) old – what can be said about conditions in the more distant past? This is a challenging question but, by putting every scrap of evidence together, it is possible to get a general idea of how the Earth's surface temperature has fluctuated during the whole of Earth history (Figure 3.18). Note that the vertical time axis counts backwards from the present day to the very earliest history of the Earth (the units being Ma – millions of years). The horizontal axis simply distinguishes only between 'colder' and 'warmer' relative to the present temperature (indicated by the vertical line) because of the difficulties in assigning accurate temperature values. Note that the last 2.4 million years (i.e. the current ice age) occupy a very small space at the top of Figure 3.18a, so the scale of this graph is inadequate for clearly showing the interglacial and glacial periods within the current ice age. Times when major ice ages occurred are identified by the (blue) horizontal shading.

### 3.4.3    So what is the fuss about?

It is clear that a variable GMST has been part of the Earth's natural behaviour, in both the recent and the ancient past. Over long periods, the fluctuation in GMST could be 10 °C or more. So is the earlier finding that the GMST has risen by somewhat less than 1 °C in the last two centuries any cause for concern? Isn't the change just a consequence of the Earth's normal behaviour? Why is the level of carbon dioxide that human activity is pumping into the atmosphere such big news, when the GMST has changed so drastically in the past, without the help of humans?

One aspect that needs to be considered when answering this question is the *rates* of increase in temperature. Look back at Figure 3.16, which shows the temperature record from the Grande Pile core for the last 140 000 years. In the last 20 000 years there has been a temperature increase of about 10 °C, and it appears that this increase took about 10 000 years to occur.

■   What rate of increase (in °C per century) does a rise of 10 °C over 10 000 years imply?

☐   A rise of 10 °C in 10 000 years is equivalent to $\dfrac{10\ °C}{10\ 000\ year}$, i.e. 0.001 °C per year, or 0.1 °C per century (to 1 significant figure).

Earlier in this chapter you calculated the GMST increase within the last 100 years or so, and found that the rate of increase was about 0.5 °C per century. Thus the current temperature increase on Earth is about five times greater than seems to have occurred in the past. It *appears* then that the recent global warming is indeed unusual. (In Book 6 you will look at some past temperature variations in more detail.) In order to understand exactly why this might be occurring, it is important to try to identify exactly what influences GMST. Thus it may be possible to unravel the causes of 'natural' changes in GMST, and consider any extra influence that human activity might be introducing. You will do this in the following chapters, starting by looking at what determines the Earth's GMST.

## 3.5    Summary of Chapter 3

The mean of a set of measurements is the sum of the measurements divided by the number of measurements.

The global mean surface temperature (GMST) is calculated (Equation 3.2) from the surface temperatures measured over a year at many sites around the world. If 30 consecutive years are averaged the effects of unusual years are reduced and long-term trends are emphasised.

Historical records (ignoring variable urban heat island effects) indicate an irregular rise in the annual GMST over the past 150 years or so, amounting to an approximate warming rate of 0.5 °C per century. Globally, the warming rate is least at the Equator (about 0.1 °C per century) and greatest near the poles (about 1.5 °C per century). This recent rate of warming appears to be unusual compared to what occurred in the past.

Any measured value has an experimental uncertainty associated with it. Random uncertainties lead to a scatter of measurements about the 'true' value, whereas systematic uncertainties lead to an offset of the measurements from the 'true' value. Measurements with small random uncertainties are said to be precise, and measurements with small systematic uncertainties are said to be accurate.

Measurements should be quoted to an appropriate number of significant figures. When reading from a scale on a piece of experimental equipment (such as a thermometer), it is convention to record a reading to the nearest half a division, and to quote the uncertainty of that reading as a value equal to half a division.

Records of fossil plant pollen can be used to estimate the mean temperature at the time the plants were alive. Fossil pollen from different depths in cores taken through peat bogs and lake beds reveals how the proportions and identities of the plants changed through time, and how climate changed through time.

The longest continuous pollen record is from France and spans the last 140 000 years but, by piecing together many different fossil records from separate places, a much longer temperature history can be established. This reveals that we are living in an ice age that started some 2.4 million years ago. Throughout this ice age, cold glacial periods have alternated with shorter interglacial periods when the climate has been warmer. The most recent glacial period ended about 10 000 years ago, and currently we are living in an interglacial period.

Ice ages lasting several tens to hundreds of millions of years have occurred at intervals throughout at least the last 2500 million years of the Earth's history.

Throughout the Earth's history, the mean temperature has changed by up to 10 °C – about 10 times greater than the increase in GMST seen in the last century or so.

In studying this chapter, you have made sense of information displayed in various images, diagrams, graphs, tables and pollen diagrams. You have plotted data on a graph. You have used SI units with various prefixes. You have considered types of uncertainty, and aspects of precision, such that you can quote values to an appropriate precision, i.e. an appropriate number of significant figures.

# Chapter 4
# What determines the Earth's GMST?

At the most basic level, the GMST is determined by the Sun – the Sun's energy keeps the Earth warm, and allows life to exist. However, you probably want a few more details than that! You need to understand *how* the Earth gains energy from the Sun, and the various ways in which it loses energy, so you can understand the processes that maintain the roughly constant temperature of today. So, this chapter starts by considering energy and power.

## 4.1   Energy and power

You will consider the concept of energy in detail in Book 3. However, it is appropriate that you learn about some aspects of energy now, as it is central to understanding what affects the GMST.

Energy is a physical property possessed by an object. There are many manifestations of energy. One of the most familiar is that associated with heat. When energy is transferred to an object, a common consequence is that the object is heated, i.e. the temperature of the object increases. When you burn gas under a pan of water, energy is transferred from the flame to the water and, as a result, the temperature of the water increases. Similarly, if you use an electric kettle to heat water, energy is transferred to the heating element from the electric current running through it, and then energy is transferred from the element to the water. When you are outside on a sunny day and turn your face to the Sun, you feel the consequence of a transfer of energy from the Sun to your skin – you feel your skin heat up. Indeed, you can detect very hot objects (an electric cooker ring, an open fire, etc.) without seeing them, just by feeling this type of heating effect. These are all examples of energy transferring from one type to another, or from one object to another. At no point is it possible to create energy or destroy energy – it can only be transferred. So, when in this chapter you read about energy *gains* and *losses* at the Earth's surface, remember it is describing the transfer of energy *to* or *from* the Earth's surface.

Energy can be measured and, therefore, it has a unit of measurement. Although there are very many forms of energy, they can all be measured in the same unit. The SI unit of energy is the **joule**, named after the British scientist James Prescott Joule (1818–1889) who made major contributions to developing the concept of energy. The symbol for the joule is J. One joule (1 J) is a small amount of energy: for example, over $10^5$ joules of energy are required to boil a kettle of water.

Power is a word that is often used in everyday life in all sorts of contexts, but it has a precise scientific meaning. Power is the *rate at which energy transfer takes place*, i.e. it is the amount of energy transferred per unit of time. This can be expressed as an equation: power = energy transferred per unit of time, or

$$\text{power} = \frac{\text{energy transferred}}{\text{time taken}} \tag{4.1}$$

You have already seen equations in previous chapters. At this stage, however, it is important to ensure that you are familiar with the overall concept of equations. If you are in any doubt, read Box 4.1 now.

## Box 4.1    Equations

An **equation** is a statement that says one quantity is the same as another quantity. Thus an equation says that one quantity is *equal to* another quantity. Written as an equation, this is expressed as:

quantity 1 = quantity 2

The term on the left of the equals sign (=) is the same as the term on the right of the equals sign. It could also be written as:

quantity 3 + quantity 4 + quantity 5 = quantity 6 + quantity 7

because it does not matter how many terms there are, or how complicated they are. The equation is still saying that all the terms on the left (in this case, quantity 3 + quantity 4 + quantity 5) are equal to the terms on the right (quantity 6 + quantity 7). A good analogy is a set of old-fashioned balancing scales: they only balance when one side is equal (in weight) to the other side. An equation is *only* valid when the two sides are balanced (i.e. equal).

You should take care with units in an equation. (The use of units was revised in Box 2.1.) For example, take the equation 3 m + 5 m = 8 m. You are no doubt happy that everything balances, i.e. add a 3 m long object to a 5 m long object and you get a combined length of 8 m. What about if you had a stick, which measured 100 cm? Could you write the following?

length of the stick = 100 cm = 1000 mm = 1 m = 0.001 km = $10^9$ nm

Yes, you could because every term represents a quantity that equals every other term. It doesn't matter that you are apparently using different units (cm, m, km, etc.), the *quantity* is still the length of the stick, expressed in the appropriate number of whatever units you choose.

Ensure you don't use an equals sign when what you really mean is 'therefore'. For example, don't write:

cost of one book = £5 = cost of ten books = £50

when you actually mean:

cost of one book = £5, therefore cost of ten books = £50

Finally, sometimes people are caught out when using the scale on a map. Imagine you have a map with a scale such that 1 cm on the map represents 1 km in reality (i.e. a scale of 1 : 100 000). You then measure a distance of, say, 9 cm between two places. As you know each cm represents 1 km in reality, you might be tempted to write 9 cm = 9 km.

However, this is *not* a valid equation. You might know what you meant but, written like this, it formally states the quantity on the left, which is a distance about the width of your hand, is equal to the quantity on the right, which is a distance about the width of a city! The correct way of expressing this is to write 9 cm on the map *is equivalent to* 9 km in reality.

The SI unit of time is the second, symbol s, and the SI unit of energy is the joule, so the SI unit of power is joules transferred per second. For example, suppose that 500 joules of energy are transferred at a constant rate, from one object to another in 20 seconds. The energy transferred per second is given by:

$$\text{power} = \frac{500 \text{ J}}{20 \text{ s}} = 25 \frac{\text{J}}{\text{s}} = 25 \text{ J s}^{-1}$$

So, in this case, the rate of energy transfer, or power, is 25 J s⁻¹. You can see that the SI unit of power is thus J s⁻¹, although another unit is used for power: the watt, symbol W (i.e. 1 W is defined as being equal to 1 J s⁻¹). The watt is exactly the same unit as that used in specifying the power requirements of electrical appliances. However, the watt is a general unit for the rate of all forms of energy transfer, not just those involving electricity.

The watt is named after the Scottish engineer James Watt (1736–1819) who, among other achievements, made major improvements to the design of steam engines, the main source of technological power in his day.

A typical microwave oven might have a power rating of 850 W. This means in one second the energy transferred is 850 J, i.e. the oven can supply energy at the rate of 850 J s⁻¹. Often it is appropriate to quote large values of power in kilowatts (kW), where 1 kW = 1000 W. (The use of prefixes with units was revised in Box 3.3.) Hence a typical electric kettle might have a rating of 2.4 kW (i.e. 2400 W).

You are now ready to consider the various rates of energy transfer – the rates of energy gain and loss – that determine the GMST. Although 'power' is an equivalent term to 'rate of energy transfer', and is shorter, the longer term will be used because it is more descriptive.

## 4.2 A balance of energy gains and losses

The GMST depends on the rate at which the Earth's surface gains energy, and the rate at which it loses energy. Note that, strictly speaking, 'surface' means the actual ground (or ocean) surface but can be extended to include the air just above it (as mentioned in Section 3.1.1).

The Sun is the ultimate source of almost all the energy gained by the Earth's surface. All other sources of energy are negligible – the next largest is the energy that flows out from the interior of the Earth, but that rate of energy flow is 2000 times less than the rate at which the surface gains solar energy. The Earth's surface loses energy by various means. For now they will be grouped together to give one overall rate of energy loss to give the highly simplified picture in Figure 4.1.

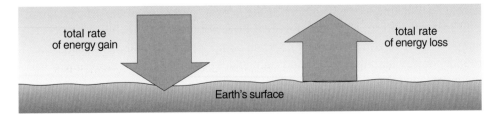
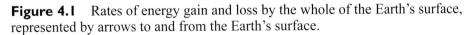

**Figure 4.1**    Rates of energy gain and loss by the whole of the Earth's surface, represented by arrows to and from the Earth's surface.

The downward-pointing arrow in Figure 4.1 represents the rate at which the whole of the Earth's surface gains energy, and the upward-pointing arrow that originates at the Earth's surface represents the rate at which the whole of the Earth's surface loses energy. Note that the width of the downward pointing arrow is equal to that of the upward-pointing arrow. This is a pictorial way of showing that the rates of energy gain and loss in Figure 4.1 are equal. A direct and important consequence of this equality is that the GMST is constant. If the rates were not equal, the GMST would change. Thus, if the rate of energy gain were to exceed the rate of loss, the excess energy input would cause a rise in GMST to a new, higher value.

■ If the rate of energy loss exceeded the rate of energy gain, what would happen to the GMST?

☐ The surface would cool to a lower GMST.

In fact, the rates are not exactly equal every second and, through the day and the year, there are moments when the gain slightly exceeds the loss, and other moments when the loss slightly exceeds the gain. However, over a period of a few years, the gains and losses largely balance out. This is why, if the GMST is averaged over a few years, the average is very nearly the same as over the previous few, or the following few, years. Therefore, the rates of energy gain and loss can be taken as near enough equal when averaged over the short term. Note that these rates can't always have been *exactly* equal, or the GMST would never have varied in the past, yet you know from Chapter 3 that it has. To explore the relationship between the GMST and the rates of energy gain and loss in more detail, it helps to begin by examining a simple analogy that shapes the behaviour of the key features of the system illustrated in Figure 4.1. This analogy will help you understand how the system works – in this sense, you are constructing a *model* of the real system.

### 4.2.1   Models in science

Insight into the behaviour of complex natural systems can often be obtained by constructing a **model**. In this context, a model is just a simplified description of something in the real world. Scientific models aid understanding by focusing only on some important aspects of the system. For example, Figure 4.2a shows an aerial image of the Walton Hall area in Milton Keynes, UK – home to The Open University's main campus. If you wanted to direct someone to a particular office, you might draw a simple sketch as in Figure 4.2b. The sketch is more usable than the photograph, and gives the person trying to find the office enough information to do so. However, Figure 4.2b is not much like reality – it is a *model* of the real situation. The important components of reality (the roads, the roundabouts, where to turn left and right and where to park) are represented in the model, and that is all that is needed.

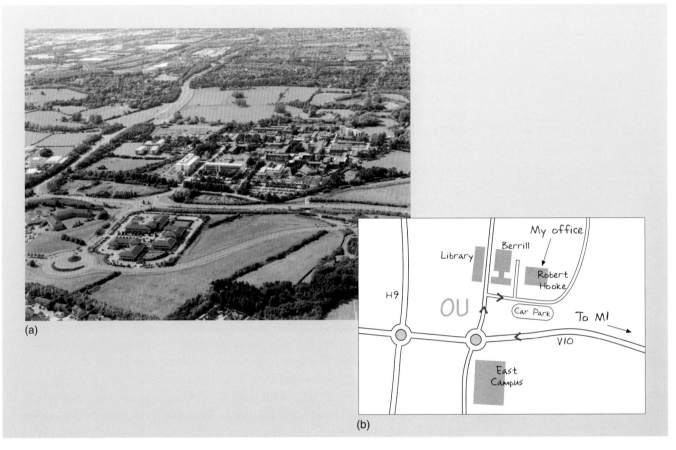

**Figure 4.2**   (a) An aerial photograph of The Open University main campus at Milton Keynes. (b) A simple sketch showing directions, which represents a model of reality.

Similarly, you may have used the London Underground (the Tube), or the New York Subway, or the Paris Metro. If so, you will know the maps are helpful but, again they are only models of reality. The distance between stations and the actual geographical locations of stations are not realistic (i.e. the map is not to scale). However, the most important information (the order of stations along the lines, and at which stations lines connect) is retained in the maps. If you required the precise layouts of roads and buildings, you would need to use a geographically accurate map. Even that map is not reality – it is just another model, but a model with somewhat different priorities. In other words, you might use different models of the same thing for different purposes.

Although the examples given here have focused on maps, a model can take many forms. Look again at Figure 4.1. You should now realise that this treatment of the balance of energy gains and losses is itself a model of the real world system. The entire Earth's surface is being represented as a single component, with a single gain and loss. Clearly, this is not like reality, but it is a model of reality that represents the main components in an understandable way. In Chapter 8 you will use a specific type of model – a mathematical model (run on a computer) – to predict changes in GMST values.

### 4.2.2    Modelling the behaviour of the GMST using a leaky tank analogy

The aim here is to *model* the behaviour of the Earth's GMST, i.e. develop a simple description of how the GMST relies on the rates of transfer of energy to and from the Earth's surface. To do this, it is useful to consider an *analogy* of the way energy transfers to and from the Earth's surface. The analogy is a leaky tank into which water is pouring.

Figure 4.3 shows a tank of water with a tap feeding water in, and a vertical slot cut in the side of the tank, letting water out. The rate at which water is fed into the tank represents the rate of energy gain by the Earth's surface; the rate at which water leaks out of the slot represents the rate of energy loss from the Earth's surface. The level of water in the tank represents the GMST: the higher the level, the higher the GMST.

In the leaky tank shown in Figure 4.3, the rate at which water flows out of the slot depends on how much water is in the tank at a given moment. The greater the depth of water in the tank, the greater the rate of water loss from the slot.

Figure 4.3a shows a sequence that starts with the tank empty, and the water flowing in at a steady rate. Initially, the leak rate is less than the rate of input, so the water level rises. The leak is through the rectangular slot at the side of the tank. As the water level rises, there is a greater length of slot to let the water out, so the leak rate increases, and it continues to increase until the leak rate equals the rate of water input. At this point, the water level stops rising, and it stays at the level it has reached. The water level is now in a **steady state**, i.e. it is not changing. Of course, water is pouring into and out of the tank, so this is a dynamic steady state rather than a static steady state. The crucial condition for the dynamic steady state is that the input and output rates are equal. This equality of rates can be expressed as:

input rate = output rate (4.2)

The graph in Figure 4.4a shows how the water level in the tank changes with time for the scenario in Figure 4.3a. You can see that in the first 10 seconds after the tap is turned on, the water level rises from zero to about 17 mm. In the time interval 10 to 20 seconds after the tap is turned on, it rises from 17 to about 30 mm, i.e. a further 13 mm in the next 10 seconds.

■ How many millimetres does the water level rise in the time interval 20 to 30 seconds after the tap is turned on?

☐ Reading from the graph in Figure 4.4a, it rises from about 30 to about 37 mm, i.e. approximately 7 mm in this next 10 seconds.

Thus, as the water level rises, the *rate* at which the level changes decreases (i.e. the rate of change in level 'slows down'). In the graph this is apparent from how the curve bends over. You can see that, ultimately, the curve flattens out and stays at the same water level – the steady-state level. At this constant level, the leak rate equals the rate of input.

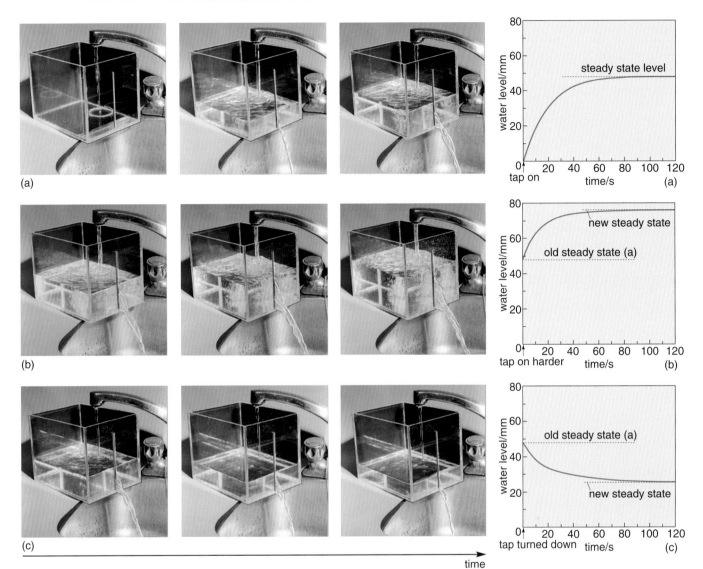

**Figure 4.3**  The leaky tank. (a) Initially the tank is empty, and the water is flowing in at a certain rate. The water level rises until the leak rate equals the rate of input, whereupon the level becomes steady. (b) The input rate is increased, and the water rises to a new steady level that is higher. (c) The input rate is decreased, and the water falls to a new steady level that is lower.

**Figure 4.4**  Graphs showing how the water level rises with time for scenarios (a), (b) and (c) in Figure 4.3.

If the tap is now turned on harder to increase the input rate, the water level starts to rise again. The leak rate increases until a new steady state is reached, with a higher water level (Figure 4.3b). The graph in Figure 4.4b shows this level to be about 76 mm. Now, returning to the original steady state at the end of the sequence in Figure 4.3a, suppose the flow from the tap is now reduced. The leak rate is now greater that the input rate, so the water level falls. This reduces the leak rate until another steady state is reached, this time at a lower water level (Figure 4.3c). The graph shows this level to be about 25 mm. So, now it is time to see how the leaky tank analogy provides an insight into the Earth's behaviour.

Figure 4.3a starts with the analogy of a cold Earth (the empty tank) and the Sun having just been turned on (the tap). The Earth's surface gains solar energy (the water) and so the GMST (the water level) rises. As it does so – and this is a crucial point – the rate of energy loss from the Earth's surface increases.

> The higher the GMST, the greater the rate of energy loss from the Earth's surface.

The reasons for this relationship between GMST and energy loss rate are explored later in the chapter. For now, the important point is that the GMST rises until the rate of energy loss by the surface equals the rate of energy gain when, as at the right of Figure 4.3a, a steady state is reached and the GMST no longer changes. This corresponds to the situation illustrated in Figure 4.1.

Figure 4.3b is analogous to an increase in the rate of energy gain by the Earth's surface, such as would follow an increase in the rate at which is the Sun emits energy. The GMST then rises until the loss rate equals the new rate of gain, another situation as in Figure 4.1, but with higher gain and loss rates.

■    What is happening to the GMST in the analogy in Figure 4.3c?

☐    In Figure 4.3c, the rate of energy gain by the Earth's surface is decreased, so the GMST falls until the loss rate equals the new, lower rate of gain.

Figure 4.5 adds these two new steady-state cases to that in Figure 4.1, along with the graphs that show the transition of the GMST from the old (original) steady state to each of the new steady states. Note that these graphs do not have quantitative scales on the axes. This would normally be a critical failing of a graph. However, when your goal is to show only the overall trend of an effect, it is permissible to do this.

So, using the leaky tank as an analogy for the way energy transfers to and from the Earth's surface, a model has been developed for the behaviour of the Earth's GMST and how it relates to the energy gains and losses of the surface. That is, given a steady rate of energy supplied to the Earth's surface, a steady state will develop where the GMST remains at a constant value. However, if the rate of energy supplied to the Earth's surface changes, a new steady state will develop, characterised by a different GMST value. So by modelling the behaviour of the system in this way, you have gained an insight to why the Earth has remained at (approximately) the same temperature for a huge period of time – it has been in a steady state – and the slight variations in GMST that have occurred in the past are a result of slightly different steady states being reached after a change in the rates of gain and loss of energy to the surface.

### Activity 4.1    Modifying the leaky tank analogy

We expect this activity will take you approximately 15 minutes.

Returning to the leaky tank, another way to influence the water level is to alter the width of the slot that controls the leak rate. If the slot is narrowed, the leak rate at any water level is less than it was before. If it is widened, the leak rate at any water level is higher than it was before.

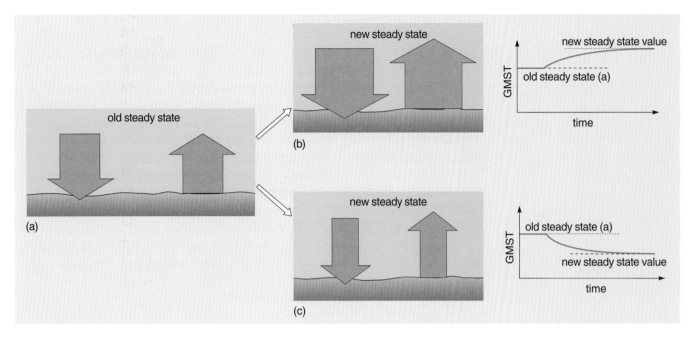

**Figure 4.5**   (a) The gain and loss of energy in the old steady state. The width of each arrow represents the rate of energy transfer. (b) The rate of energy gain by the Earth's surface is increased, and the GMST rises until a new steady state is reached. The rate of energy transfer is higher than the old steady state. (c) When the rate of energy gain by the Earth's surface is decreased, the GMST falls. The rate of energy transfer is lower than the old steady state.

With the aid of Figures 4.4 and 4.5, describe what happens to an initially steady water level when the rate of water flow from the tap is constant, but the rectangular slot is (a) narrowed; and (b) widened.

Your description in each case should consist of several sentences, plus diagrams showing the tank at the start and finish, and a sketch graph (similar to the style of those in Figure 4.5 without any values on the axes) showing how the water level changes with time.

Now look at the comments on this activity at the end of this book.

As you will see in the next section, the processes by which the Earth's surface gains and loses energy are very different from the processes by which the tank gains and loses water, but the analogy should help you to understand that:

- the rate of energy loss from the Earth's surface increases as the GMST rises, and decreases as the GMST falls

- a steady-state GMST requires the rate of energy gain by the Earth's surface to equal the rate of energy loss

- if the steady state is disturbed in any way, but there is no further disturbance, a new steady state is ultimately established, with a different GMST.

## 4.3    The rate of energy gain from solar radiation

The energy that streams out from the Sun is called **solar radiation**. Radiation in general terms means something that spreads out (radiates) from a source. There are several completely different types of radiation that come from the Sun, but the energy that is transferred from the Sun to the Earth is dominated by an extremely important type – visible light or **visible radiation**. This is just one part of a very broad range of light-type radiation (you will consider the full range in detail in Book 3). The light that is visible to humans can be split into different colours (as in a rainbow), and the colour perceived is actually a property of the wavelength of the light. Don't worry about the physical meaning of wavelength now – you will study this in Book 3 – but just consider wavelength to be a property of light that relates to its colour. Figure 4.6 shows the range of visible radiation displayed as the colours of the rainbow. It also shows in which direction the wavelength property increases (longer wavelengths) and decreases (shorter wavelengths). Human eyes are sensitive to only the visible radiation (light) but if you could see light of a shorter wavelength, you would be able to detect **ultraviolet radiation**, which lies just beyond violet. Similarly, if you could see light of a longer wavelength, you would be able to detect **infrared radiation**, which lies just beyond red. (Note that ultraviolet and infrared are often abbreviated to UV and IR, respectively.)

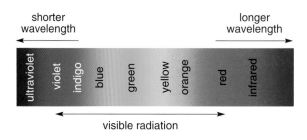

**Figure 4.6**    The range of visible radiation displayed as the colours of the rainbow. The direction of shorter and longer wavelengths – ultraviolet (UV) radiation and infrared (IR) radiation – are also shown.

Although UV radiation is not visible, many people are familiar with the effect it has on their skin – it can give a suntan (or, indeed, if you over do it, sunburn). This is why the information on creams to prevent sunburn often refers to UV filters, which reduce the intensity of the UV radiation that reaches the skin. Similarly, infrared radiation is not visible but can also be detected indirectly in that, when infrared radiation is absorbed by skin, it heats the skin. When the element of an electric cooker is turned up to full, it glows red ('red hot'). It is emitting red light but it is also emitting a lot of infrared radiation, which causes the feeling of warmth on your skin even if you are a long way from the cooker. In fact, all objects emit infrared radiation; it is just most obvious when they are very hot (i.e. the intensity of the infrared radiation is related to the temperature of the object). This is why infrared cameras allow the world to be seen even in total darkness. Like everything else, the ground radiates infrared radiation – a fact that you will see is crucial in the next section.

Returning to solar radiation: as mentioned above, most of the energy transfer occurs through visible radiation but a significant amount is also transferred through ultraviolet and infrared radiation. The radiation leaving the Sun spreads out in all directions, and a very small proportion of it reaches the Earth.

■ What is the SI unit for the rate at which energy leaves the Sun in the form of solar radiation?

☐ The SI unit for the rate of transfer of any form of energy is the watt, so the unit of energy transfer through solar radiation is also the watt (or $J\ s^{-1}$).

A large power station generates about $10^9$ W of electrical power, and all the power stations in the world generate rather less than $10^{13}$ W. The Sun is far more powerful: it emits solar radiation at the impressive rate of $3.85 \times 10^{26}$ W. This power is called the **solar luminosity**.

As the radiation from the Sun spreads out in all directions, some of it reaches the top of the Earth's atmosphere at all places on the side of the Earth facing the Sun (Figure 4.7). This side can be represented as a disc-shaped area facing the Sun, shown with pale shading in Figure 4.7. The rate at which solar radiation falls on this area is obtained from measurements taken by radiation sensors on satellites orbiting the Earth. (It is necessary to go into space because the Earth's atmosphere absorbs much of the intercepted solar radiation.) An area of one square metre (1 m²) facing the Sun (as in Figure 4.7) intercepts about 1370 W of solar radiation. In other words, 1370 W per square metre, or 1370 W m⁻², is intercepted. This is a mean value over many years, the actual value varying slightly from moment to moment (because of random variations in the Sun's surface) and from season to season (because the Earth-to-Sun distance changes slightly throughout the year – the further away the Earth is from the Sun, the less radiation is intercepted). This average value is called the **solar constant**. The word constant is perhaps somewhat misused because of the slight variations mentioned above; however, it is conventional to use the term solar constant.

The disc-shaped area in Figure 4.7 that faces the Sun is obviously *much* larger than 1 m² – in fact, it is $1.27 \times 10^{14}$ m². The total solar radiation intercepted by the Earth can then be calculated from:

total solar radiation intercepted = solar constant × area of disc (4.3)

You can then substitute the values into this equation to give:

total solar radiation intercepted = 1370 W m⁻² × $1.27 \times 10^{14}$ m²
= $1.74 \times 10^{17}$ W

Note that multiplying the units W m⁻² by m² gives W because:

$$\mathrm{m^{-2} \times m^2 = \frac{1}{m^2} \times m^2 = \frac{m^2}{m^2} = 1}$$

The total amount of solar radiation intercepted is also a mean value, for the same reasons that the solar constant is a mean value.

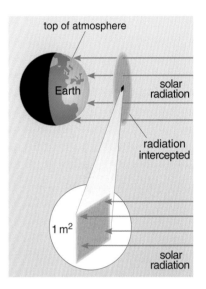

**Figure 4.7** Earth intercepts the amount of solar radiation that falls on the shaded disc-shaped area facing the Sun. An area of 1 m² within this disc (shown greatly magnified at the bottom of the diagram) receives (on average) 1370 W of solar radiation. The diameter of the Earth is much smaller than the distance from the Earth to the Sun, so the 'rays' from the Sun are almost parallel.

Not all of this intercepted radiation reaches the Earth's surface. To see why, the fate of solar radiation as it passes through the Earth's atmosphere to the Earth's surface must be examined.

## 4.4    Solar radiation in the Earth's atmosphere and at its surface

The Earth's atmosphere significantly affects incoming solar radiation, partly because of the gases that constitute the atmosphere and partly because of atmospheric aerosols. An **aerosol** is a collection of tiny (typically micrometre-sized) liquid or solid particles dispersed in a gas, such as water droplets in the atmosphere (inside or outside clouds). Atmospheric dust is another example of an aerosol, in this case consisting of solid particles. The aerosol spray from a can consists of tiny liquid droplets.

As solar radiation passes through the Earth's atmospheric gases and aerosols, it is subject to two processes that each reduce the amount reaching the Earth's surface (Figure 4.8). Figure 4.8a illustrates the process of **absorption** of solar radiation by atmospheric gases and aerosols. The essential feature of absorption is that solar radiation is ultimately converted into heat, which causes a rise in the temperature of the atmospheric gases and aerosols.

Figure 4.8b illustrates the other atmospheric process of **scattering**. Here, atmospheric gases and aerosols don't absorb solar radiation but redirect it. Scattered radiation travels in all directions. Some escapes back to space, and the rest reaches the Earth's surface by an indirect route. Clouds are particularly good at scattering, but so too are some other aerosols. Scattering and absorption occur throughout the atmosphere, although particularly in the lower levels where most of the mass of the atmosphere is concentrated, as you will see in Chapter 5.

**Figure 4.8**    (a) Absorption of solar radiation by the Earth's atmosphere. (b) Scattering of solar radiation by the gases and aerosols in the Earth's atmosphere. (c) Reflection of solar radiation by the Earth's surface. (d) Absorption of solar radiation by the Earth's surface.

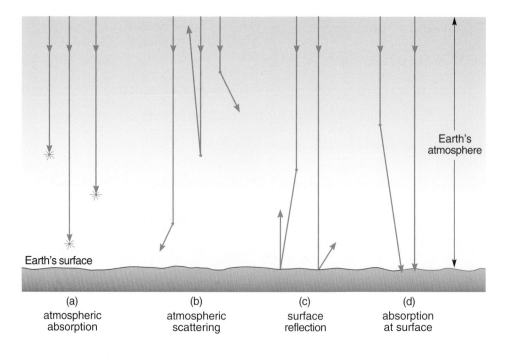

The solar radiation that escapes absorption or scattering back into space reaches the Earth's surface. Some of this radiation is scattered from the surface (Figure 4.8c). In this case, because the Earth is so dense, the radiation is not scattered in all directions but only back into the atmosphere. This is usually called **reflection**, although essentially it is the same as scattering. Different types of surface reflect different proportions of solar radiation. Ice and snow reflect most of it, whereas the oceans reflect very little.

The radiation reaching the Earth's surface that is not reflected is absorbed (Figure 4.8d). In the oceans this happens throughout the top few tens of metres of water, whereas on the land it is confined to a much thinner surface layer. Just as in the atmosphere, the absorbed solar radiation gives rise to an increase in the surface temperature. In other words, the Earth's surface is radiantly heated by the Sun. Figure 4.9 shows the mean rates of energy transfer that involve solar radiation in the Earth's atmosphere and at the surface, in terms of the percentage of the total incoming solar radiation (which in Figure 4.9 is 100%).

You can see from Figure 4.9, that of the 100% of total incident solar radiation, 20% is absorbed by the atmosphere, 49% is absorbed by the Earth's surface, and 31% is returned ('escapes') to space. This 31% that escapes back to space, consists of two components – the solar radiation reflected from the Earth's surface (9%) and the solar radiation scattered by the atmosphere (22%).

The mean rate at which solar radiation is returned to space by the combined effects of scattering and reflection, expressed as a proportion of the total initially intercepted by the Earth, is called the **albedo** (sometimes also called the Bond albedo). The word albedo is derived from the Latin word *albus*, meaning white. For example, if a surface has an albedo of 0.6 (or 60%), this means that 60% of radiation falling on the surface is reflected.

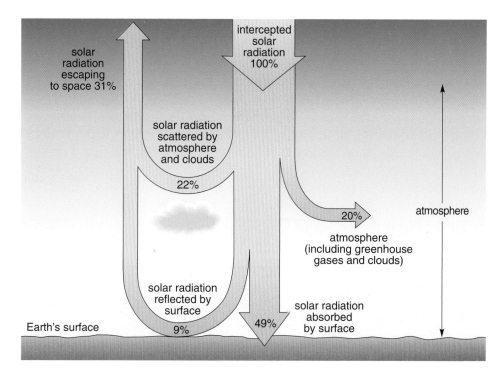

**Figure 4.9**  Energy transfer rates (shown as a percentage of the total incoming rate) involving solar radiation in the Earth's atmosphere and at its surface. The width of each arrow indicates approximately the relative rate of energy transfer.

■ If 31% of the radiation intercepted by the Earth is reflected back to space, what is the albedo of the Earth?

□ The albedo of the Earth is 31%, or 0.31.

## 4.5    The rate of energy loss from the Earth's surface

Having considered energy gains made by the Earth's surface, it is now time to consider energy losses. There are three major ways in which the Earth's surface loses energy: one is radiation from the surface, and the other two depend on a process called convection occurring in the atmosphere.

### 4.5.1    Convection

Convection carries energy away from the Earth's surface through currents of air rising upwards. However, it helps to look at this process first in the simpler case of liquids. Consider a pan of water at room temperature standing on a switched-off electric hot-plate, as in Figure 4.10a. There is no upward or downward motion in the water, and the temperature and density of the water are the same throughout its volume. **Density** is defined as the mass per unit volume of a substance, i.e.:

$$\text{density} = \frac{\text{mass}}{\text{volume}} \tag{4.4}$$

■ What is the SI unit of volume and thus density?

□ The unit of volume is m$^3$ and thus the unit of density must be $\dfrac{\text{kg}}{\text{m}^3}$, i.e. kg m$^{-3}$.

Different materials have very different densities: for example, the density of water is 1000 kg m$^{-3}$; the density of gold is 19 300 kg m$^{-3}$; the density of air (dry air near sea level) is 1.2 kg m$^{-3}$.

Now suppose that the situation in Figure 4.10a is disturbed by switching on the hot-plate (Figure 4.10b). This heats the base of the pan, which causes its temperature to rise. The base of the pan in turn heats the thin layer of water in contact with it, causing the water's temperature to rise. The water in this layer is heated by a process called **conduction**. This is the transfer of heat from a region of higher temperature (the base of the pan) to a region of lower temperature (the bottom layer of water) because of the direct contact between the two regions. A familiar consequence of conduction is the rising temperature of a metal teaspoon's handle when you stir a cup of hot tea.

**Figure 4.10**    A pan of water (a) before it is heated and (b) when it is heated from below, showing convection.

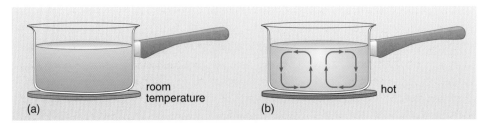

The rise in the temperature of the thin layer of water causes it to increase in volume. This is called **thermal expansion**, which is a phenomenon displayed by all liquids, and by solids and gases too.

■ What will happen to the density of the thin layer of water when it expands? (Note that its mass is fixed.)

☐ From Equation 4.4, if the mass is fixed but the volume increases, the quantity $\frac{mass}{volume}$ decreases, and thus the density will decrease.

The thin layer of water now has a lower density than the water above it. From experience, you know that a lower density solid floats on a higher density liquid (ice, most woods and polystyrene in water being good examples).

■ What will happen to the lower density solid if it is pushed under the liquid?

☐ It will rise back to the surface.

So, you should expect the warmed water with its reduced density to rise upwards, which it does, displacing the overlying cooler, denser water downwards. In principle this could happen in several different ways. It could happen on a microscopic scale, with tiny uprising threads of warm water and tiny descending threads of cooler water. However, it happens on a larger scale, and Figure 4.10b shows the approximate pattern of motion. A steady cycle is set up, with warmed water rising to the surface, displacing the cooler water downwards where it is warmed in turn and also rises. Meanwhile, the water that had risen has cooled, and is then displaced downwards by the rising warmer water. Fluid flow driven by temperature differences is called **convection**, and Figure 4.10b shows one example.

Having touched on thermal expansion, it is timely to note one often misunderstood mechanism for sea-level rises. As mentioned in Chapter 2, a consequence of the increase in GMST is that the sea level is rising. Many people assume that this is caused only by ice melting. However, it is currently dominated by the thermal expansion of the oceans as they warm up.

Melting of ice does have an effect, but most of our ice is (thankfully) still 'locked up' in Greenland and Antarctica. Ice melt has certainly had a great effect in the past when ice ages have ended and vast numbers of mountain glaciers have melted and deposited huge amounts of water into the oceans. However, this is not as straightforward as might first appear. If ice sheets that are sitting on top of land (as in Greenland and Antarctica) were to melt, the meltwaters would flow into the ocean and contribute to a sea-level rise. Indeed, if all the ice on Greenland and Antarctica melted completely, the sea level would rise by over 70 m! Conversely, ice in the form of sea ice or ice shelves that *float* on the ocean surface (such as Arctic sea ice in winter, or ice shelves around the coast of Antarctica, or icebergs) would not make a significant contribution to a sea-level rise if it melted. This is basically because no extra mass of water is being added to the ocean – the water is already there as ice. The fact the ice rises up above the surface of the ocean does not matter. This is simply a result of the ice being less dense than water, so a given mass of water, when frozen, occupies a larger volume and so 'sticks up' above the surface.

To clarify this, think of the *volume* of an iceberg that lies *below* the surface. This is sometimes referred to as the volume of water displaced by the iceberg. If this displaced volume were actually occupied by the surrounding water, that water would have a mass exactly equal to the mass of the entire iceberg. This is a physical requirement of floating, first realised by the mathematician Archimedes, over 2000 years ago. When the whole iceberg melts, the resulting meltwater remains the same overall mass, but returns to having the same density as the surrounding water, and thus this meltwater would fill the displaced volume exactly (essentially like filling in a hole without altering the surrounding sea level). This is why floating ice cubes melting in a jug of water do not alter the level of the water as they melt. (This answers the first of the questions posed at the beginning of Chapter 1.) In fact, when it comes to ice on oceans, there is an effect to do with a difference in density between fresh meltwater and saltwater that leads to a slight rise in sea level, but it is only a very small effect and usually ignored.

For the GMST, the relevant feature of convection in a liquid in a pan is that it transfers energy away from the base of the pan at a considerably higher rate than if there were only conduction through the liquid. If the heated base of the pan represents the radiantly heated Earth's surface, and the water represents the Earth's atmosphere, you can see that conduction of heat from the Earth's surface into the atmosphere in contact with the surface will give rise to convection. Through this process, the Earth's surface will lose energy at a considerable rate, and the atmosphere will gain energy at a corresponding rate. Atmospheric convection can often be seen as the shimmer (or heat haze) from the heated air rising from a hot surface such as a road in sunlight (Figure 4.11), or above a central heating radiator or a toaster. The effect of hot air rising is used by balloonists. The burner heats the air enclosed by the balloon canopy to the point where it becomes sufficiently buoyant to lift the canopy, the basket and its occupants.

**Figure 4.11**  Visible heat haze above a hot surface caused by heated air rising rapidly by convection.

Convection does not happen everywhere at the Earth's surface at all times but, when it does, the pattern at any instant at a particular place is typically as in Figure 4.12: there are columns of rising air, with much larger regions of descending air between them. This pattern can exist on scales that, at ground level, range from a few centimetres across to many metres. The rising air loses energy to its surroundings, and is subsequently displaced downwards. Columns of convection are so gentle that they usually go unnoticed, although glider pilots use them to carry the glider upwards. Glider pilots call them thermals. Some birds also use thermals for lift.

**Figure 4.12**  Convection patterns in the Earth's atmosphere. Warm air rises, transferring energy away from the Earth's surface to the atmosphere. Cooler air is displaced downwards.

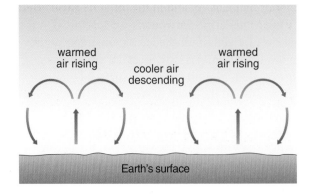

## 4.5.2   Latent heat

In addition to conveying warmed air upwards, convection plays an essential role in a quite different mechanism of energy loss by the Earth's surface. This involves the **evaporation** of liquid water to produce water vapour (i.e. gaseous water). Convection carries this water vapour upwards, enabling more water to evaporate from the surface. The source of this surface water is not just seas and lakes (and rivers) but any moisture at the surface, such as damp soil or vegetation. Ice can change state directly from solid to water vapour by a process called **sublimation**, and this too contributes to the water vapour in the atmosphere.

But how does evaporation remove energy from the Earth's surface? Evaporation requires energy to be transferred to the liquid (or ice) in order to produce the water vapour. This energy is called **latent heat**. This latent heat energy doesn't increase the temperature (which is why the word latent is used, meaning hidden), but it changes the state of the substance; in this case, from liquid or solid to gas (water vapour). While the water undergoing a change of state does not change its temperature, the water (or ice) left behind at the surface *will* decrease in temperature. This is because the latent heat has been extracted from the material, so the water (or ice) that supplied it decreases its temperature. You will be familiar with this effect. Try dampening the palm of your hand with a liquid, and then wave it vigorously to promote evaporation – the cooling should be obvious. The evaporation of sweat in a strong wind also produces obvious cooling. This cooling effect is caused by the moisture requiring latent heat (i.e. energy) to turn into water vapour, so it extracts the energy from your skin, which has a cooling effect. Similarly, evaporation of water from the Earth's surface will tend to cool the surface.

Air heated by the ground rises up through the atmosphere. As it rises, its temperature decreases. If the temperature falls low enough, some of the water vapour in the air condenses to form a large number of liquid droplets or icy particles – clouds. This is because the amount of water vapour that air can contain is related to the temperature of the air. The higher the temperature, the more water vapour the air can hold. Another way of saying this is that, at any given temperature, there is a maximum amount of water vapour that can stay in the air. When this maximum is reached, the air is said to be saturated. Of course, the air is not always saturated, and the term used to express how close to saturation it is, is **relative humidity**. If the relative humidity is, for example, 50%, the mass of water held in the air is half of what it would contain if it were saturated. The amount of water vapour that can be held in the air at its **saturation point** (i.e. 100% relative humidity) depends on temperature. The higher the temperature, the more water vapour the air can hold. This is an important point that has consequences for the greenhouse effect – you will return to this in Chapter 8.

Returning to the (moist) air that, having been heated by the ground, is rising up through the atmosphere; it probably started its journey upwards considerably below its saturation point (i.e. relative humidity less than 100%). However, as the air rises and the temperature drops, eventually the saturation point is reached, the air cannot hold all the water as vapour, so some condenses to liquid droplets, producing clouds. Indeed, puffy clouds often appear in rising columns of air.

If it takes an input of heat to produce vapour from liquid or solid, you might expect heat to be given out in the condensation of vapour to produce liquid and solid, which is the case. The latent heat energy given out by condensation heats the surrounding atmosphere. The evaporation and condensation of water thus transfers energy from the Earth's surface to the Earth's atmosphere. Ultimately, precipitation returns the condensed water to the ground, mostly as rain or snow, where it is susceptible again to evaporation or sublimation (Figure 4.13).

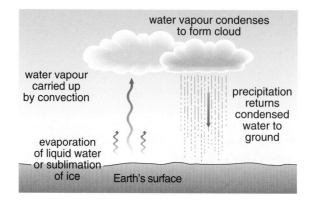

**Figure 4.13**    Clouds forming in rising columns of air, a consequence of water vapour carried upwards by convection. This water vapour is evaporated from the Earth's surface, which consequently loses energy via latent heat. When the water vapour condenses, the latent heat is given out and raises the temperature of the surrounding atmosphere. Energy is thus transferred from the Earth's surface to the atmosphere. Precipitation from the atmosphere returns water to the ground (i.e. as rain or snow).

### 4.5.3    Infrared radiation emitted by the Earth's surface

As mentioned in Section 4.3, all objects emit infrared radiation. The Earth's surface thus emits infrared radiation, carrying energy away from the surface and cooling the surface. Although convection is an important means by which the Earth's surface loses energy, the emission of infrared radiation accounts for the greatest loss of energy from it. The infrared radiation emitted by the Earth's surface is either absorbed by the atmosphere (so heating the atmosphere) or lost to space.

Question 4.1

In two or three sentences, explain why atmospheric convection helps to reduce the level of atmospheric pollution at the ground (pollution from vehicle exhausts, industrial processes, etc.).

Question 4.2

If at a particular time there is no convection over a region of the Earth's surface, and no wind, explain in a few sentences why the surface in that region can lose little energy by way of latent heat.

## 4.6 Atmospheric infrared radiation absorbed by the Earth's surface

So far in this chapter, you have read about transfers of energy from the Sun to the Earth's atmosphere and surface, and from the Earth's surface to the atmosphere and space. Focus just on the energy absorbed by the Earth's atmosphere.

■ What are the four sources of energy that heat the atmosphere?

☐ They are absorbed solar radiation, energy transferred from the Earth's surface by convection, latent heat (energy) given out when water vapour condenses, and absorbed infrared radiation emitted from the Earth's surface.

So, the atmosphere absorbs energy from various sources, and this energy gain sustains the atmospheric temperature. Of course, the atmosphere itself must emit infrared radiation, just as the Earth's surface does. This 'atmospheric infrared radiation' is emitted in all directions, and some of it escapes to space. The rest ultimately reaches the ground and thus constitutes another energy gain by the surface, to add to solar radiation. However, it is important to realise that atmospheric infrared radiation is ultimately derived from solar radiation. This is because all of the four energy gains by the atmosphere depend on solar radiation: the atmosphere is warmed by the Sun directly; it is also warmed indirectly by convection, latent heat, and surface emission of infrared radiation, all of which arise from the heating of the Earth's surface by solar radiation. Therefore, the energy gain by the Earth's surface is always dominated by solar radiation, whether it is direct or indirect.

Figure 4.14 brings together the various processes that have been considered so far. The upward-pointing leftmost arrow represents the rate at which energy is transferred from the Earth's surface to the atmosphere through convection and latent heat. The wide arrow on the right leaving the Earth's surface represents the rate at which infrared radiation is emitted by the Earth's surface. This arrow splits into two, producing a thin arrow representing the small amount of emitted radiation from the Earth's surface that escapes directly to space, and a thicker arrow which curves over and ends in the atmosphere.

■ What does this curved arrow represent?

☐ It represents the rate at which infrared radiation emitted by the Earth's surface is absorbed by the atmosphere.

The two other arrows originate in the atmosphere, and represent the infrared radiation emitted by the atmosphere. The upward-pointing arrow represents the rate at which infrared radiation emitted by the atmosphere escapes to space, and the downward-pointing arrow represents the rate at which infrared radiation emitted by the atmosphere is absorbed by the Earth's surface. Note that, even though the arrows starting and stopping in the atmosphere do so in a small region in the centre of the figure, the atmospheric energy gains and losses take place throughout the whole atmosphere.

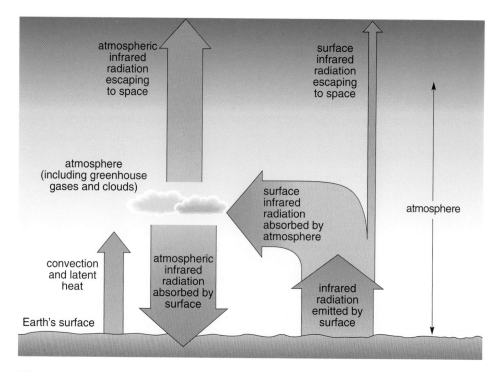

**Figure 4.14**   Exchanges of infrared radiation involving the Earth's surface and its atmosphere. The convective and latent heat transfers are also included. The width of each arrow indicates approximately the rate of energy transfer.

## 4.7   What determines the GMST?

You have now met all of the important energy gains and losses at the Earth's surface. The time has come to put them all together and obtain an overview, so that you can see the processes that determine the GMST.

### 4.7.1   An overview of energy gains and losses

Figure 4.9 represents how the Earth's surface (and atmosphere) absorbs solar radiation, and Figure 4.14 represents how energy is lost from the Earth's surface (and atmosphere). This 'energy in–energy out' system requires these processes to be considered simultaneously, which Figure 4.15 does (i.e. it is a combination of Figures 4.9 and 4.14). The key points can be summarised as follows.

- The left-hand side of Figure 4.15 (the four connected arrows) shows the rates of energy gain and loss by the Earth's surface and atmosphere that involve solar radiation *directly*.

- In the centre of Figure 4.15, the arrow labelled 'convection and latent heat' shows the rate of energy transfer from the Earth's surface to the atmosphere by a combination of convection and latent heat.

- The remaining arrows in Figure 4.15 (on the right of the figure) show infrared radiation only. At the extreme right (three connected arrows), infrared radiation is emitted by the Earth's surface, some of it escaping directly to space, and the rest (the major part) being absorbed by the atmosphere. The atmosphere then re-emits infrared radiation, some of which escapes to space, the rest being absorbed by the Earth's surface.

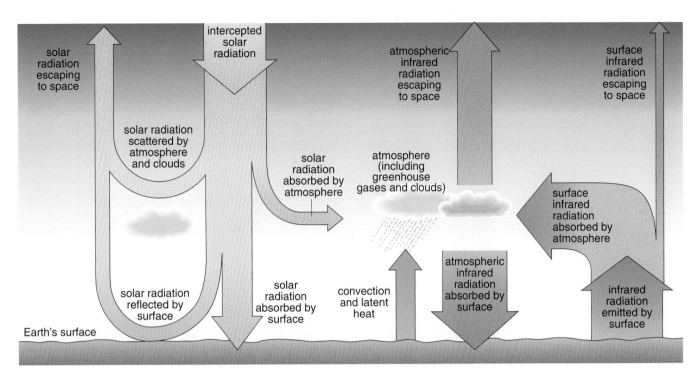

**Figure 4.15**   Energy gains and losses by the Earth's surface and atmosphere. Note that, even though the arrows starting and stopping in the atmosphere do so in a small region in the centre, the atmospheric energy gains and losses that they represent take place throughout the atmosphere. The width of each arrow indicates approximately the rate of energy transfer.

In the next activity you will reinforce your understanding of Figure 4.15 by labelling a different form of the diagram.

## Activity 4.2   Flow diagram for the energy gains and losses in the Earth's atmosphere

We expect this activity will take you approximately 15 minutes.

Figure 4.16 summarises the energy flows that determine the Earth's GMST. This is a **flow diagram** and such diagrams are a particularly useful way of summarising information. You will meet many examples of flow diagrams throughout the course and you will develop further, the skill of constructing your own flow diagrams. To develop this ability, you should convert Figure 4.15 into a flow diagram. To help you, the basic outline of the flow diagram is shown in Figure 4.16 as a set of lines connecting four boxes. The lines represent the energy transfers between the different boxes, one of which has been labelled. Your task is to add the labels to the other lines. Try to do this at first without referring to Figure 4.15.

**Figure 4.16** Flow diagram summarising the energy flows that determine the Earth's GMST.

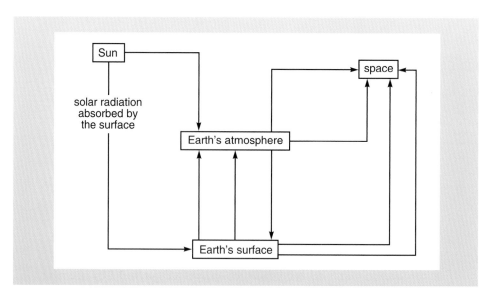

Now look at the comments on this activity at the end of this book.

### 4.7.2   Why the GMST has a particular value

In broad terms, you can see from Figure 4.15 that the value of the GMST depends on the following factors.

- The rate at which Earth intercepts solar radiation: this rate is obtained by multiplying the area over which radiation is intercepted (the shaded disc in Figure 4.7) by the solar constant.

- The properties of the atmosphere, particularly those that influence:

     the scattering and absorption of solar radiation

     the absorption by the atmosphere of the infrared radiation emitted by the Earth's surface

     the emission of infrared radiation by the atmosphere

     the rate of energy transfer by convection and latent heat.

- The properties of the Earth's surface, particularly those that influence:

     the reflection and absorption of solar radiation

     the emission of infrared radiation by the surface

     the availability of water for evaporation.

If any of these factors is changed, the GMST may change. Currently, the GMST is in a steady state. If a factor changed, the GMST would change – eventually reaching a new steady state.

Now you will examine the case of the solar constant, and carry out a 'thought experiment', i.e. think hypothetically about an experiment – even if it is

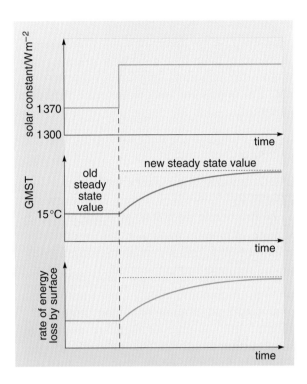

**Figure 4.17**  Response of the GMST to a sudden increase in the solar constant at a particular time (indicated by the dashed vertical line), and the consequent increase in the rate of energy loss from the Earth's surface. Note that the solar constant axis does not start at zero, so the solar constant is increased only slightly.

impossible to do the experiment in reality. Suppose that initially there is a steady state with the Sun shining as it does today when, suddenly, you 'flick a switch' which increases the solar constant to a slightly higher value, with no change in atmospheric and surface properties. This is represented by the top graph in Figure 4.17, which shows the sudden increase in the value of the solar constant at a particular time. What would happen? At once, the Earth's surface would receive more solar radiation than before and, because the surface would absorb the same fraction of this radiation, it would therefore absorb a greater overall amount of solar radiation. At the instant that the solar constant changed, there would be no change in the rate of energy loss by the surface, so the GMST would start to rise, as shown in the middle graph in Figure 4.17. This rise in GMST would cause the surface to emit more infrared radiation, so the rate of energy loss would increase as the temperature increased, as shown in the bottom graph in Figure 4.17. If there were no atmosphere, the GMST would continue to rise until the rate at which energy was lost by the surface equalled the new rate of energy gain by the surface. There would then be a new steady state, the GMST being higher than before. (This is basically the situation in the leaky tank analogy in Figure 4.4b.)

The presence of an atmosphere complicates the situation because the surface also receives infrared radiation from the atmosphere, and loses energy through convection and latent heat. However, the outcome would be similar, i.e. an increase in the solar constant would cause an increase in the GMST.

The solar constant does indeed vary. Recall that the value quoted earlier (Section 4.3) is an average value over many years. The solar constant varies by only about 0.1% over a decade or so, although the changes can be larger in the longer term. Variations in the solar constant have been a contributory factor to the variations in the GMST in the ancient past, but there are many other ways of disturbing the steady state. This chapter concludes by considering just one more – the effect on the GMST of changing the rate at which the atmosphere absorbs and emits infrared radiation. This brings you back to the much publicised greenhouse effect touched on in Chapter 2.

## 4.8    The greenhouse effect

In Section 4.7 you saw how the GMST depends on various factors but is generally in a steady state, unless one of the factors is changed (when a new steady state will be reached). You saw that one of the factors affecting the steady state is the properties of the atmosphere. In fact, the atmosphere is *the* critical component giving rise to the greenhouse effect. This section considers why this is, to help you understand exactly what the greenhouse effect is.

How does the atmosphere give rise to the greenhouse effect? Look again at Figure 4.15. The leftmost group of arrows depict the fate of the incoming solar radiation; some of it is absorbed by the Earth's surface, i.e. a gain of energy. This warms the surface, which in turn emits infrared radiation (the rightmost group of arrows), i.e. a loss of energy. If Earth had no atmosphere, that would be the whole story. There would be a steady state, with the Earth's surface reaching a temperature (GMST) such that the rate of energy loss equalled the rate of energy gain.

However, Earth *does* have an atmosphere, and that changes the picture substantially. Now, a proportion of the infrared radiation emitted by the surface is absorbed by the atmosphere, which then re-emits infrared radiation, some of which is absorbed by the Earth's surface. So the Earth's surface now has another source of heating (i.e. infrared radiation from the atmosphere), so it gets hotter than it would if there were no atmosphere. This leads to a higher steady-state GMST than there would be without an atmosphere. This effect, whereby the presence of an infrared-absorbing atmosphere leads to a higher GMST, is called the **greenhouse effect**.

The greenhouse effect gets its name from the fact that, in a garden greenhouse, the air temperature inside is greater than outside. In fact, much of this difference in temperature has nothing to do with the greenhouse effect described above. It simply arises from the containment of warm air that would otherwise convect upwards and be replaced by cooler air. However, a small part of the difference is because the glass panes in a greenhouse behave rather like the Earth's atmosphere with respect to infrared radiation (Figure 4.18). The panes of glass are transparent to the visible light component of the incident solar radiation, but not the ultraviolet and infrared components. Some of the visible light is absorbed by the ground (and plants) inside the greenhouse, which heats the ground (and plants). The ground then emits infrared radiation, but this infrared radiation cannot pass through the glass, which absorbs and then re-radiates the infrared radiation. Some of this infrared radiation is emitted back into the greenhouse (the rest being radiated outwards to the outside world), which leads to a further heating of the ground. Thus the glass effectively traps infrared radiation, and thus

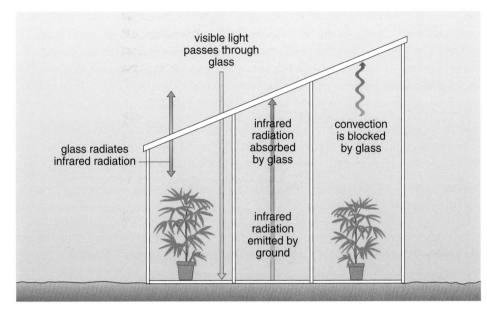

**Figure 4.18**   How a greenhouse can be warmer than the surrounding air. In reality, the major increase in temperature in a greenhouse is caused by the blocking of convection of warm air (indicated in the figure); however, the 'greenhouse effect' refers to the role of infrared radiation and how it is absorbed by the glass and partly radiated back into the greenhouse by the glass.

heat, inside the greenhouse, giving rise to a higher steady-state temperature than if the glass were not there.

The Earth's greenhouse effect is crucial for the continuing success of life on Earth. The current GMST is about 15 °C. This allows liquid water to exist over much of the Earth's surface – liquid water being critical for life in general. However, if the atmosphere did not absorb infrared radiation, the GMST would be about –20 °C, i.e. the Earth's surface would *not* have liquid water, with catastrophic consequences for life. You can see that the greenhouse effect is a good thing, which makes the bad press it often gets seem a little unfair! However, as is often the case, you can have too much of a good thing. If the atmosphere could somehow absorb more infrared radiation than it does now, and thus radiate more infrared back to the Earth's surface, the GMST would be higher than it is now.

The more absorbing to infrared radiation the atmosphere is, the higher the GMST will be.

Clearly, if the GMST was too high, life on Earth would suffer as a consequence. This, of course, is at the heart of the concerns about global warming.

So you can see that the amount of infrared radiation the atmosphere can absorb is critical in determining the final steady-state GMST. The effectiveness of the atmosphere to absorb infrared radiation is called the **infrared absorptivity**. The higher the absorptivity, the more infrared radiation the atmosphere can absorb, and thus the higher the steady-state GMST will be.

So, is the infrared absorptivity of the Earth's atmosphere constant over time? Not necessarily – a change in the constituents of the atmosphere could increase the infrared absorptivity, and thus increase the GMST. It turns out that increasing the proportion of certain gases, such as carbon dioxide, will increase the atmosphere's infrared absorptivity, and thus increase the GMST. So, there is the link between gases such as carbon dioxide and the GMST.

The next chapter looks at the constituents of the atmosphere, and why certain constituents contribute to the infrared absorptivity of the atmosphere, and are thus important in determining (or changing) the Earth's GMST.

Before moving on, you need to return to the activity on measuring precipitation and then review your progress.

---

### Activity 2.1 (continued)    Measuring precipitation – Part 2

We expect this activity will take you approximately 15 minutes.

Analysis of results (at the end of week 1)

You have probably gathered one week of rain gauge data by now. If not, return to this activity when you have data for a week.

*Task 4    The mean daily precipitation for week 1*

Use the data you entered into Table 2.2 to calculate the precipitation for *each* day measured by the two rain gauges (see the comments on Task 1), and enter these values in rows 4 and 6 of the table, for week 1. Then calculate the mean daily precipitation in your neighbourhood for week 1 for each gauge and write in the values in the spaces below the table. (The method of calculating the mean is exactly the same as you used for calculating the mean surface temperature in Section 3.1.1.)

*Uncertainties in the measurements*

As discussed in Section 3.1.2, scientists generally quote the experimental uncertainties associated with their measurements. It was recommended that you measure depths to the nearest 0.5 mm, i.e. to a precision of half a graduation (assuming a typical ruler has 1 mm graduations).

- ■  How would you express the experimental uncertainty in this depth?

- ☐  The experimental uncertainty would usually be quoted as being equal to half the value of a graduation. So, the uncertainty is ±0.5 mm. Thus a measurement may be written as, for example, 4.0 mm ± 0.5 mm.

So, the uncertainty in each of your daily values of precipitation is about ±0.5 mm. In Section 3.1.2, you were also advised to use the same value of uncertainty when quoting the mean.

Now look at the comments on Task 4 at the end of this book.

---

## Activity 4.3  Reviewing your progress

We expect this activity will take you approximately 15 minutes.

Much research has been done on people's learning styles, and how effective different styles are for different people. Clearly, being aware of how you are going about your learning, and thinking about how you could improve your learning experience, can be very beneficial. So, in this activity you should think about how well you are learning from the course material.

(a) Look at your study plan from Activity 1.1. Are you on schedule, ahead of it, or behind it? Scan through the remaining chapters of this book, and make any revisions to your study plan that might be necessary. If you think you are behind, what could you do to get back on schedule?

(b) You also need to consider whether you have been using your time effectively. This means more than just keeping to a schedule (and that can be difficult enough, as you have probably found out). Answering the following questions will help you to review how effectively you are studying.

   (i) Identify a part of the material you have studied so far, where you feel your learning went really well. Why did it go so well? Was it because of the type of material or the time of day you were studying, or because you were feeling particularly fresh? Do you think you have developed a preferred style of study yet?

   (ii) Identify a part of the material you have studied so far, where you think your learning went less well. Why do you think it went less well? Again, was it because of the type of material, because you were tired, or because you kept being interrupted?

(c) At the beginning of this book you were strongly encouraged to interact with the text by highlighting, making notes, summarising or representing text in the form of diagrams, explaining it in your own words, and so on. This is called active reading because it is so different from sitting passively reading a book. We strongly encourage you to keep up this active reading throughout the rest of the course.

   (i) Have you been doing anything that you think amounts to active reading? If so, what?

   (ii) Do you feel that the active reading techniques might have helped you remember or understand better?

Reflect on these issues, and then look at the comments on this activity at the end of this book. You may also like to discuss the issues raised in this activity with your tutor.

## 4.9   Summary of Chapter 4

The Sun is the ultimate source of almost all of the energy gained by the Earth's surface. The Earth's surface gains energy by absorbing a large fraction of the intercepted solar radiation, and by absorbing most of the infrared radiation emitted by the atmosphere.

Power is the rate of energy transfer. The SI unit for energy is the joule (J), and the SI unit for power is the joule per second ($J\,s^{-1}$), also called the watt (W).

A model can often be used to gain insight into the behaviour of complex natural systems. Scientific models aid understanding by focusing only on particular important aspects of the system.

A leaky tank of water is a useful analogy for the energy gains and losses at the Earth's surface, and the corresponding GMST. In this analogy:

- the rate at which water flows into the tank represents the rate at which the Earth's surface gains energy
- the rate at which water flows out of the tank represents the rate at which the Earth's surface loses energy
- the level of the water in the tank represents the GMST.

The behaviour of the leaky tank leads to a model for the Earth's GMST, i.e. given a steady rate of energy supplied to the Earth's surface, a steady state will develop where the GMST remains at a constant value. In the steady state, the rate of energy gain by the Earth's surface equals the rate of loss and, therefore, GMST does not change. However, if the rate of energy supplied to the Earth's surface changes, a new steady state will develop, characterised by a different GMST value.

The GMST is raised considerably (by over 30 °C) because of the greenhouse effect. This effect depends on atmospheric greenhouse gases that absorb most of the infrared radiation emitted by the Earth's surface.

The more absorbing to infrared radiation the atmosphere is (i.e. the higher its infrared absorptivity), the higher the GMST will be.

In studying this chapter, you have had practice in explaining in words some aspects of your study. You have used flow diagrams. You have considered the concepts of analogies and models in science. You have reviewed your progress and reflected on your learning.

# Chapter 5
# The Earth's atmosphere

## 5.1   The structure of the Earth's atmosphere

The atmosphere consists of a mixture of gases (including water vapour) with aerosols mixed in. Unlike substances in the solid or liquid state, the molecules in a gas are free to move about randomly. The molecules collide with each other and with surfaces they encounter. Indeed, it is the collisions of the molecules with a surface that exert a pressure on the surface, i.e. the gas is pushing against the surface (Figure 5.1).

There are many units used to express pressure. An old-style unit, which is still used to describe such things as the pressure in car tyres, is pounds per square inch or psi. The pressure of the atmosphere at sea level (sometimes described as 'one atmosphere') is about 15 pounds per square inch. This means that the pressure is equivalent to having a 15 pound weight (about 7 kg) pushing down on every square inch (about 6 cm$^2$) of surface. Of course, it is not just the case that the pressure of the atmosphere pushes down against the ground – atmospheric pressure applies in all directions, against any surface. Indeed the atmosphere itself is supported by the pressure of its own gas. This is why the atmosphere doesn't simply collapse into a thin layer near the ground under the action of gravity – the pressure of the gas near the ground pushes against the overlying atmosphere, preventing it from compressing into a thin, dense layer. (This answers another of the questions posed at the start of Chapter 1.)

A unit of pressure commonly used is the bar, where 1 bar (or 1000 millibars) is the pressure of the Earth's atmosphere at sea level. This unit (particularly millibars) is often used in relation to weather forecasts. However, the SI unit of pressure is the pascal, symbol Pa. The atmospheric pressure at sea level is typically about $1.0 \times 10^5$ Pa (i.e. 1 bar is equivalent to $10^5$ Pa). However, the pressure rapidly decreases with altitude. This is because there are fewer molecules of air per unit volume, so fewer collisions and thus a lower pressure – pressure is directly related to the number of molecules per unit volume. Table 5.1 gives you an idea of the number of air molecules per unit volume, i.e. per m$^3$ (note that per m$^3$ becomes units of m$^{-3}$), and the resulting pressure at various altitudes. You can see from Table 5.1 that the number of air molecules per unit volume decreases rapidly above 1 km. By 10 km, the number has fallen to 33% of the value at sea level. By 40 km, it has fallen to just 0.34% of the sea-level value.

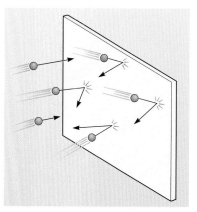

**Figure 5.1**   A gas exerts a pressure on a surface as a result of collisions. Each impact of a molecule with the surface is analogous to a ball hitting a racquet or bat.

**Table 5.1** Number of air molecules per unit volume, and air pressure, at different altitudes.

| Altitude/km | Number of air molecules/m$^{-3}$ | Air pressure/Pa | Proportion of sea-level value/% |
|---|---|---|---|
| 0 (sea level) | $2.6 \times 10^{25}$ | $1.0 \times 10^{5}$ | 100 |
| 1 | $2.2 \times 10^{25}$ | $8.9 \times 10^{4}$ | 85 |
| 10 | $8.7 \times 10^{24}$ | $2.8 \times 10^{4}$ | 33 |
| 40 | $8.9 \times 10^{22}$ | $3.2 \times 10^{2}$ | 0.34 |
| 80 | $5.2 \times 10^{20}$ | 1.3 | $2.0 \times 10^{-3}$ |
| 120 | $1.2 \times 10^{18}$ | $4.6 \times 10^{-3}$ | $4.6 \times 10^{-6}$ |
| 160 | $3.8 \times 10^{16}$ | $2.7 \times 10^{-4}$ | $1.5 \times 10^{-9}$ |

So, what is the thickness of the atmosphere? It's quite hard to answer this. The number of molecules per unit volume continues to decrease, but doesn't reach zero, so there isn't really a defined edge to the atmosphere. However, typically, the thickness of the atmosphere might be said to be about 100 km, in that if you were in a spacecraft returning to Earth, you would not notice the atmosphere at all until about 100 km above the Earth's surface, at which point you would start to feel the effects, i.e. the air would start slowing down the spacecraft, and cause heating from friction. Indeed, meteoroids – small fragments of rock that come from asteroids and comets – entering the Earth's atmosphere burn up (i.e. are heated by the friction to the point of vaporisation) at an altitude of between 70 km and 100 km. So 'about 100 km' is about as precise as you can be about the thickness of the atmosphere. However, most of the atmosphere (in terms of number of molecules) lies below an altitude of 10 km. It is in this region of the atmosphere that most of the infrared radiation emitted from the Earth's surface is absorbed. It is also the region where most of the effects recognised as weather are experienced. This region of the atmosphere is called the **troposphere** (Figure 5.2). The region above it is called the **stratosphere**. The troposphere is fairly well-mixed, i.e. gases and aerosols released at sea level will rapidly disperse into the troposphere.

**Figure 5.2** Cross-section of the Earth's surface and its atmosphere. The troposphere extends to about 10 km above sea level, with the stratosphere above it extending to about 50 km. Other layers above this are not shown here.

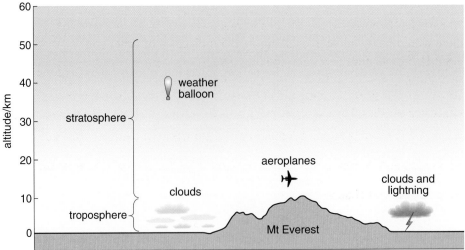

## 5.2   The composition of the Earth's atmosphere

The air contains many different types of molecule, some of which play an important role in the Earth's greenhouse effect. Table 5.2 gives information about the composition of a typical sample of air at sea level. Air consists almost entirely of nitrogen and oxygen, with smaller amounts of argon, water vapour and carbon dioxide. In Table 5.2 the percentage composition based on the number of molecules is different from the percentage composition by mass, because the different types of molecule have different masses. Question 5.1 will help to show you why these percentages are different.

**Table 5.2** Gaseous composition of a typical sample of the Earth's atmosphere at sea level in 2004 (main components only).

| Component | Number of molecules/m$^{-3}$ | Proportion of total number/% | Proportion of total mass/% |
|---|---|---|---|
| nitrogen | $2.0 \times 10^{25}$ | 77.6 | 75.5 |
| oxygen | $5.4 \times 10^{24}$ | 20.9 | 23.2 |
| argon | $2.4 \times 10^{23}$ | 0.93 | 1.28 |
| water vapour* | $1.3 \times 10^{23}$ | 0.5 | 0.3 |
| carbon dioxide | $9.7 \times 10^{21}$ | $3.8 \times 10^{-2}$ | $5.6 \times 10^{-2}$ |

\* This is highly variable, so typical values are given.

Question 5.1

Figure 5.3 shows a mixture of large blue and smaller red particles. Each red particle has a mass of 1 g, whereas the blue particles each have a mass of 10 g. Calculate the percentages of red and blue particles in the mixture based on (a) the numbers of particles and (b) their masses.

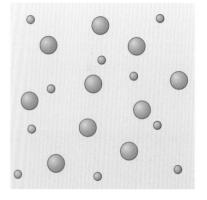

**Figure 5.3**   A collection of 10 small red particles of mass 1 g each, and 10 large blue particles of mass 10 g each.

The third column of Table 5.2 shows that if you took a sample of 100 molecules of air then, on average, there would be about 78 molecules of nitrogen and 21 molecules of oxygen. This use of percentages is like saying 'parts per hundred'. For example, the 78% nitrogen represents a fraction $\dfrac{78}{100}$ of the total or 78 parts per hundred. Table 5.2 also suggests that, per 100 molecules of air, there would be 0.9 molecules of argon, 0.5 molecules of water and $3.8 \times 10^{-2}$ molecules of carbon dioxide. This is less helpful, because there is no such thing in reality as a fraction of a molecule; it reflects the choice of 100 molecules as the starting point. For such small proportions, it is better to use **parts per million**. For example, the $3.8 \times 10^{-2}$% of carbon dioxide represents $3.8 \times 10^{-2}$ (i.e. 0.038) parts per hundred. As a fraction of the total, this is $\dfrac{0.038}{100}$, but the top and bottom terms can be multiplied by 10, and the overall value of the fraction does not change, i.e.:

$$\frac{0.038}{100} = \frac{0.38}{1000} = \frac{3.8}{10\,000} = \frac{38}{100\,000} = \frac{380}{1\,000\,000}$$

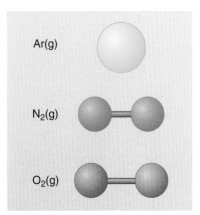

**Figure 5.4** Three of the gaseous elements of air, shown in the ball-and-stick representation. Argon exists as single atoms, but nitrogen and oxygen both exist as pairs of atoms. Pale blue, dark blue and red are used to distinguish the atoms of argon, nitrogen and oxygen, respectively.

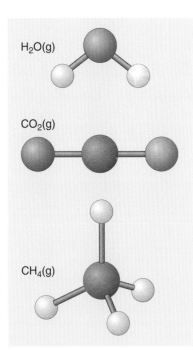

**Figure 5.5** Ball-and-stick representations of water ($H_2O$), carbon dioxide ($CO_2$) and methane ($CH_4$). Red represents atoms of oxygen, white hydrogen, and grey carbon.

and, as 1 000 000 is a million, the 0.038 parts per hundred has become 380 parts per million, or 380 ppm.

■ Table 5.2 shows that the percentage of argon molecules in air is 0.93%. Express this as a fraction, and as a proportion in ppm.

☐ To convert 0.93% into a fraction, divide by 100, i.e. $\dfrac{0.93}{100}$.

To convert this fraction into ppm, multiply it by a million:

$$\frac{0.93}{100} \times 1\,000\,000 = 0.93 \times 10\,000 = 9300 \text{ ppm}$$

Of course, it is sensible to use the most appropriate tool for the job. So, a discussion of the proportions of nitrogen and oxygen would favour the use of percentages. However, when discussing the proportions of the minor constituents in the atmosphere (such as carbon dioxide), it is more appropriate to use parts per million. Indeed, if the proportion is *very* small, even parts per billion (ppb) might be more appropriate; one billion being $10^9$. For example, the concentration in the atmosphere of the greenhouse gas nitrous oxide is at a level of $3.15 \times 10^{-5}\%$, i.e. 315 ppm. The concentration of another greenhouse gas, methane, is at a level of $1.75 \times 10^{-4}\%$, i.e. 1750 ppb.

The molecules of the main components of the atmosphere are considered here because the properties of some gases are important in understanding the greenhouse effect and global warming. Of the gases listed in Table 5.2, only argon is a molecule that comprises just one atom (i.e. the atom *is* the molecule). Nitrogen and oxygen are molecules that comprise two atoms. These three molecules are shown in Figure 5.4 as ball-and-stick representations. The balls represent the atoms and the sticks represent the bonds between the atoms that hold the molecules together. Molecules and bonding are considered in detail in Book 4 but, at this stage, this simple representation is fine. Indeed, this ball-and-stick representation is another example of using a model to represent reality. The elements argon, nitrogen and oxygen are written as chemical symbols Ar, N and O respectively. As shown in Figure 5.4, molecules of argon gas, nitrogen gas and oxygen gas should be written as chemical symbols Ar(g), $N_2$(g) and $O_2$(g), respectively.

The two other gases listed in Table 5.2 (water and carbon dioxide) are molecules made of more than one type of atom. Water comprises one oxygen (O) atom and two hydrogen (H) atoms. Carbon dioxide comprises one carbon (C) atom and two oxygen atoms. Thus molecules of water gas (i.e. water vapour) and carbon dioxide gas are written as chemical symbols $H_2O$(g), and $CO_2$(g) respectively. In addition, methane comprises one carbon atom and four hydrogen atoms, thus the molecule of methane gas is written as $CH_4$(g) – see Figure 5.5 for ball-and-stick representations of $H_2O$(g), $CO_2$(g) and $CH_4$(g). If you are not entirely clear about the use of chemical symbols (or the difference between elements, atoms and molecules), read Box 5.1 now. (You will learn more about why molecules are shaped the way they are in Book 4.)

## Box 5.1  Elements, atoms, molecules and chemical symbols

Everything around you – all materials, whether living or non-living – are made up of a combination of **chemical elements**, or just **elements** for short. Each chemical element consists of just one type of atom. There are over 100 different elements in nature and each has its own chemical symbol. Table 5.3 lists 30 of the more common elements you might be familiar with, and their chemical symbols.

**Table 5.3**  Thirty well-known chemical elements and their chemical symbols.

| | | |
|---|---|---|
| aluminium, Al | iodine, I | phosphorus, P |
| argon, Ar | iron, Fe | potassium, K |
| calcium, Ca | lead, Pb | silicon, Si |
| carbon, C | magnesium, Mg | silver, Ag |
| chlorine, Cl | mercury, Hg | sulfur, S |
| copper, Cu | neon, Ne | sodium, Na |
| chromium, Cr | nickel, Ni | tin, Sn |
| gold, Au | nitrogen, N | titanium, Ti |
| helium, He | oxygen, O | tungsten, W |
| hydrogen, H | platinum, Pt | zinc, Zn |

Atoms are the smallest individual particles of an element – an atom being roughly $10^{-10}$ m across (a page in this book is about 200 000 atoms thick). A molecule is formed when one or more atoms (of either the same or a different type) are bonded together into a slightly larger unit. For example, a molecule of nitrogen gas consists of two nitrogen atoms. This is written $N_2$ (pronounced N-two); note the 2 is subscript. So, a subscript number *after* a chemical symbol tells you how many atoms of the element there are.

If there is a number written *in front of* a chemical symbol, this tells you how many molecules there are. For example, carbon dioxide has the molecule $CO_2$ (pronounced C-O-two) and so has one atom of carbon and two atoms of oxygen; whereas carbon monoxide (which incidentally has very different properties from carbon dioxide) has the molecule CO, and, if you saw 2CO, it would mean $2 \times (CO)$, i.e. two molecules of CO, which results in a total of two atoms of carbon and two atoms of oxygen.

Question 5.2

How many atoms of each element are present in $H_2O$, $2H_2O$, $C_{12}H_{22}O_{11}$ and $3C_{12}H_{22}O_{11}$?

Finally, when writing the chemical symbols for a substance, the convention is to indicate whether it is a solid, liquid or gas, by writing (s), (l) or (g) after the molecule. For example, carbon dioxide gas is $CO_2(g)$; water, $H_2O$ (pronounced H-two-O), might be experienced in everyday life in all three states, i.e. $H_2O(s)$ is solid ice, $H_2O(l)$ is liquid water, and $H_2O(g)$ is water vapour or steam.

## 5.3   The greenhouse gases

Recall from Section 4.8, the basis of the greenhouse effect – the atmosphere absorbs infrared radiation emitted from the Earth's surface, and then it re-radiates infrared radiation, some of which goes towards extra heating of the surface (thus increasing the GMST). The key is that the atmosphere absorbs some infrared radiation; as mentioned in Section 4.8, the effectiveness of the atmosphere in absorbing infrared radiation is called the infrared absorptivity. The higher the absorptivity, the more infrared radiation the atmosphere can absorb (and re-radiate), and thus the higher the steady-state GMST will be. A **greenhouse gas** is a gas that can absorb infrared radiation, so contributing to the greenhouse effect. Not all gases can do this. The atmosphere absorbs infrared radiation only because certain gases in the mixture that makes up air are greenhouse gases.

A greenhouse gas molecule can absorb infrared radiation in two ways. The chemical bonds that hold molecules together are not so much like the rigid sticks used in the ball-and-stick model, but are more like springs. And, like springs, they can vibrate, as shown in Figure 5.6 for water. When the bond (or spring) absorbs energy from the infrared radiation, it vibrates more energetically. However, infrared radiation is absorbed *only* if a molecule contains more than two atoms, or – if it contains only two atoms – the atoms at each end of the bond are of different elements.

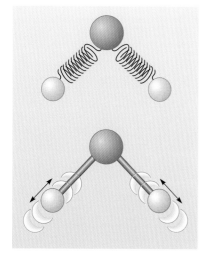

**Figure 5.6**   A water molecule in which the bonds are represented as springs (top figure). The double-headed arrows show how the bond can vibrate (lower figure).

■   Which of the atmospheric constituents in Table 5.2 can absorb infrared radiation through changes in their vibration? (Figures 5.4 and 5.5 may help you to decide.)

☐   Argon exists as single atoms and so has no bonds and can't absorb infrared radiation. Oxygen and nitrogen molecules consist of two atoms of the same type, so these molecules can't absorb infrared radiation. Molecules of carbon dioxide and water both contain two types of atom – so these molecules can absorb infrared radiation through changes in the way they vibrate.

The second way in which molecules can absorb infrared radiation is via rotation of the molecule. If infrared radiation is absorbed, the molecule will rotate faster. However, of the atmospheric gases listed in Table 5.2, only water vapour can absorb infrared radiation in this way. (It is to do with the fact the molecule is not straight – see Figure 5.5 – but the precise reason is beyond the scope of this course.)

To conclude, nitrogen, oxygen and argon do not absorb infrared radiation, so they will not behave as greenhouse gases. However, water vapour and carbon dioxide *do* absorb infrared radiation and so they are greenhouse gases. This is an amazing result! The predominant gases in the Earth's atmosphere – nitrogen and oxygen – which together account for almost 99% of the atmosphere, make no contribution at all to the greenhouse effect. Two minor components – carbon dioxide (0.038%) and water vapour (0.5%) – give rise to the majority of the atmosphere's infrared absorptivity, and thus almost all of the contribution to the increase in GMST attributed to the greenhouse effect. In fact, the largest contribution (about 60%) is made by water vapour.

Question 5.3

The atmosphere of Venus is about 97% carbon dioxide. The Venusian atmosphere contains far more molecules per cubic metre than the Earth's atmosphere. Would you expect there to be a greenhouse effect on Venus? If so, how would it compare with that on Earth?

## 5.4    The processes of recycling

Clearly, the amounts of water vapour and carbon dioxide in the atmosphere are very important. The atmosphere's infrared absorptivity depends on how many water molecules and carbon dioxide molecules are present; the more molecules present, the greater the proportion of radiation absorbed. Table 5.2 records the proportion of water vapour and carbon dioxide in the atmosphere, and these proportions help to give rise to the current GMST, which is about 15 °C. How much would these proportions of water and carbon dioxide in the atmosphere have to change before the GMST changes significantly – or even catastrophically? To understand this, you need to know what controls the small, but crucially important, amounts of water vapour and carbon dioxide in the atmosphere. This requires an understanding of how water and carbon substances move around the Earth, being cycled through many different places over time.

We live on a dynamic planet. Substances in the air, in the oceans and on land are continually being made, or broken down, turned into other substances, transported, and so on. While the total amount of material that makes up Earth is essentially constant, various substances are perpetually changed or recycled. Indeed, recycling processes are most important at the Earth's surface, where you live and, in terms of the climate, the most important recycling processes are those concerned with water and with carbon. It is through these recycling processes that the amounts of water vapour and carbon dioxide are maintained at an approximately steady level. It is also through these recycling processes that a change in a part of the system can result in changes in the level of water vapour and carbon dioxide in the atmosphere.

In the next two chapters you will explore the 'water cycle' and the 'carbon cycle' and see how these cycles affect the climate.

**Activity 5.1    Summary of the Earth's atmosphere**

We expect this activity will take you approximately 15 minutes.

Summarising is an important skill. Before you look at the chapter summary in the next section, make your own brief summary of what you now know about the Earth's atmosphere. A good way of doing this is to make two lists, one headed 'Composition' and the other 'Properties'. Initially, try noting down points from memory. Then look back through Chapter 5 and add to the list as you are reminded of others. This will give you practice in picking out the important information from a piece of text.

Now look at the comments on this activity at the end of this book.

## 5.5    Summary of Chapter 5

The Earth's atmosphere is a mixture of gases: mainly nitrogen and oxygen, with minor constituents argon, water vapour and carbon dioxide. It also contains aerosols.

The pressure and the number of molecules per cubic metre of the atmosphere decrease with increasing altitude.

Molecules can be represented by ball-and-stick models.

Greenhouse gases are gases that can absorb (and thus re-emit) infrared radiation, so contributing to the greenhouse effect.

Although oxygen and nitrogen, the predominant gases in the Earth's atmosphere, do not absorb infrared radiation, two minor constituents – carbon dioxide (0.038%) and water vapour (0.5%) – do absorb infrared radiation, and are the main greenhouse gases.

In studying this chapter, you have seen how to express the amount of a substance that is present in a small proportion, as parts per million, ppm (or parts per billion, ppb). You have used chemical symbols (including state symbols) to represents elements and molecules. You have also summarised the key points of a section.

# Chapter 6    The water cycle

In Chapter 5 you saw that, although there is only a relatively small amount of water vapour in the Earth's atmosphere, the fact that it absorbs infrared radiation means that it has a major effect on the GMST. Indeed, water vapour is the main greenhouse gas.

■  In which other way does water vapour in the atmosphere influence the GMST?

☐  Water vapour in the atmosphere can form clouds, which reflect solar radiation and so reduce the amount of solar radiation that reaches the ground.

Clearly, you need to look at what influences the amount of water vapour in the atmosphere and whether this amount varies in the short and the long term. This in turn requires an examination of how water gets into and out of the atmosphere. First, you will look at how water is distributed on Earth.

## 6.1    Reservoirs

Water exists in various forms on Earth: as the gaseous state (water vapour) in the atmosphere; as liquid water droplets or solid ice crystals in clouds; as liquid water in oceans, lakes, rivers and underground; and as solid ice in snow, glaciers and ice sheets.

Table 6.1 shows how the water on Earth is distributed. Each type of location where water resides is called a **reservoir**. Hence the term 'reservoir' does not mean a single physical mass of water that is used, say, to provide mains tap water. Rather the term is a means of collecting under one heading all water in a particular *type* of location, irrespective of its geographical position. (The term does not have to relate to water either – in the next chapter it is also applied to carbon.) Table 6.1 shows the total mass of water (second column) that resides in each of the reservoirs. Note that the heading is labelled '/$10^{15}$ kg' meaning that the values in the column must be multiplied by $10^{15}$ kg; for example, the value 2 in this column means $2 \times 10^{15}$ kg. (You first met this sort of labelling in Figure 3.16.) Note also that the majority of the values given in the second column will not then be in strict scientific notation, as scientific notation requires the first number to be equal to or greater than 1, but less than 10. (This was explained in Box 3.2.)

■  How would $43\,000 \times 10^{15}$ kg be written in proper scientific notation?

☐  It would be written $4.3 \times 10^{19}$ kg.

**Table 6.1**  Earth's major reservoirs of water.

| Reservoir | Mass of water/$10^{15}$ kg | Proportion of total water/% | Residence time |
|---|---|---|---|
| ocean | 1400 000 | 96 | about 3000 years |
| ice and snow | 43 000 | 2.9 | about 10 000 years |
| underground water | 15 000 | 1.0 | a few weeks to 10 000 years |
| lakes | 360 | 0.025 | about 10 years |
| soil moisture | 80 | 0.005 | a few weeks to 1 year |
| atmosphere | 15 | 0.001 | about 11 days |
| plants and animals | 2 | 0.000 14 | a few days to several months |
| rivers | 1 | 0.000 07 | a few weeks |

Table 6.1 (and some other figures and tables throughout the next two chapters) use powers of ten notation but depart from strict scientific notation, to make it easier to compare values at a glance. For example, it is obvious that $15\,000 \times 10^{15}$ kg is 15 000 times greater than $1 \times 10^{15}$ kg, whereas comparing $1.5 \times 10^{19}$ kg with $1 \times 10^{15}$ kg takes a little more thought. Table 6.1, as well as showing the total mass of water that resides in each of the reservoirs, also shows the corresponding percentage of the total (third column). The fourth column, residence time, you will return to shortly.

You can see from Table 6.1 that the vast majority of water is in the oceans, as you might expect. The next biggest reservoir is ice and snow. It is perhaps somewhat surprising to find that underground water is a much bigger reservoir than all the water held in lakes. Indeed, there is a vast amount of water held in subsurface rocks. This is not, as you might expect, in large underground caves, but mainly within the rocks themselves. Rocks often contain pores or cracks into which water can seep, and most of the underground reservoir of $15\,000 \times 10^{15}$ kg are stored in this way. Perhaps the most surprising information in Table 6.1 is that there is about double the amount of water held in plants and animals than in all the Earth's rivers!

While Table 6.1 focuses on the reservoirs, the water cycle is all about the transfer of water between these reservoirs. Indeed, once a molecule of water is in a particular reservoir, it is only a matter of time before it will be transferred to another reservoir. The average time that a water molecule spends in any one reservoir is called the **residence time**, which is also given in Table 6.1 (fourth column).

## 6.2    Transfers between reservoirs

One of the more obvious ways in which you can see water being transferred within the water cycle is when it rains. The more general term is precipitation, which includes any form of water – liquid or solid – that originates from the atmosphere and ends up on the ground. Examples include rain, hail, snow, dew and frost. Indeed, you are probably measuring the precipitation in your local area, as part of the ongoing rain gauge activity (Activity 2.1). Clearly, the amount of precipitation will vary over the Earth's surface. Figure 6.1 shows the mean annual precipitation (in millimetres) around the world.

## Question 6.1

At the end of Chapter 4, you analysed the first week of your precipitation data from Activity 2.1. You will have calculated a value for the mean daily precipitation based on the first week's measurements.

(a) What would you expect the annual precipitation to be, if this mean daily precipitation occurred every day of the year?

(b) How does this value compare with the values indicated for your region in Figure 6.1?

(c) Would you expect the annual precipitation calculated in this way to match that given for your region in Figure 6.1? (If not, why not?)

The global mean annual precipitation (a quantity analogous to the global mean surface temperature) is about 1000 mm. This means that the equivalent of 1000 mm (i.e. 1 m) depth of water is distributed over the entire globe every year. So why doesn't the sea level rise by 1 m or more each year? It is because the

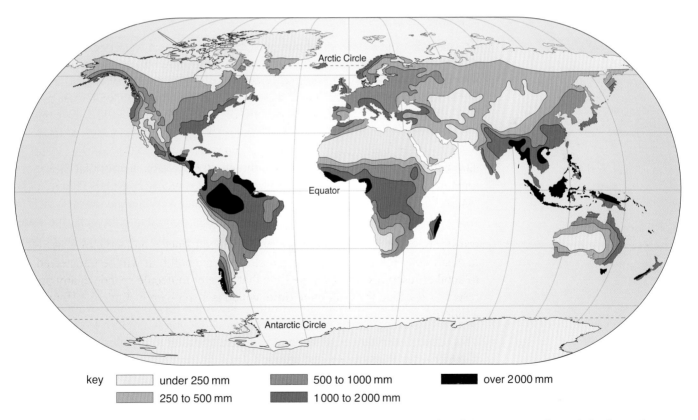

key   under 250 mm        500 to 1000 mm        over 2000 mm
      250 to 500 mm       1 000 to 2 000 mm

**Figure 6.1** A map of Earth with various shaded (colour) areas representing the mean annual precipitation values experienced around the world. Some of the wettest regions on Earth (equatorial regions) can experience mean annual precipitation of over 2000 mm.

amount of water that leaves the atmosphere as precipitation each year is balanced by the amount of water that leaves the land and oceans by evaporation. This dynamic state, where water is exchanged between the Earth's surface (i.e. the two reservoirs, land and ocean) and the atmosphere is summarised as a flow diagram in Figure 6.2.

■ What do you notice from Figure 6.2 about the rates of precipitation and evaporation?

☐ The rate at which water leaves the atmosphere in the form of precipitation is the same as the rate at which water enters the atmosphere by evaporation.

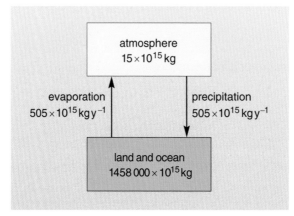

**Figure 6.2**   Flow diagram showing the balance between water leaving the atmosphere by precipitation and water entering the atmosphere by evaporation. The numbers in the boxes refer to the amount of water in that particular reservoir in kilograms. The numbers on the arrows refer to the rate of movement of water from one reservoir to another in kilograms per year. To make comparisons easier, all the numbers are written with the same power of ten, $10^{15}$.

This balance of water entering and leaving the atmosphere ensures that the amount of water in the atmosphere remains approximately constant. This is similar to the leaky tank analogy you met in Chapter 4. When the rate at which water left the tank matched the rate at which water poured into the tank, the water level remained constant, i.e. there was a steady state. However, even though the amount of water in the atmosphere is relatively constant, you must remember that the system is a dynamic one with water continuously entering and leaving the atmosphere. The rate at which water enters the atmosphere by evaporation is strongly related to the local temperature – the hotter it is, the more evaporation there is (assuming the air is not already saturated – you will return to this later). This reflects everyday experience; it is generally easier to dry clothes on a sunny summer's day than an overcast winter's day.

The scenario shown in Figure 6.2 combines the land and ocean reservoirs. However, the exchanges over land and over ocean are somewhat different. Over land, it is not just evaporation that transfers water to the atmosphere. Plants draw water from the soil *below* the surface via their roots. This water is then carried up through the stems to the leaves. The surface of the leaves has many tiny pores, called stomata, through which the water comes in contact with the air, and can thus evaporate. This whole process is called **transpiration**. One result of transpiration is that nutrients are transported with the water from the roots to the stems and leaves. Another result is that significant amounts of water are moved from the soil to the air. A large oak tree, for example, transpires on average about 400 litres of water a day when in full leaf.

Figure 6.3 shows the same scenario as in Figure 6.2, but now with the exchange processes separated into the atmosphere over land and the atmosphere over ocean. The atmosphere–ocean exchange is the same as before, in that the transfers are via precipitation and evaporation. However, the atmosphere–land exchange has precipitation, and a combination of evaporation and transpiration. As before, the mass of water in each reservoir is indicated with values based on those in Table 6.1. The water transfer rates are also shown, and the situation is more complicated than in Figure 6.2.

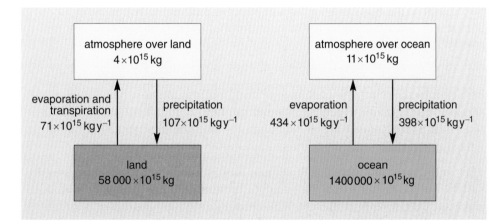

**Figure 6.3**   Flow diagram showing the exchange of water between the atmosphere and land and the atmosphere and ocean. The numbers in the boxes refer to the mass in kilograms of water in that particular reservoir. The numbers on the arrows refer to the movement of water from one reservoir to another in kilograms per year.

■   Look again at Figure 6.3, concentrating on just the land environment. What do you notice about the numbers on the arrows that indicate the movement of water from the land to the atmosphere and vice versa?

☐   They do not balance. The values indicate that each year $107 \times 10^{15}$ kg of water move from the atmosphere to the land as precipitation, but only $71 \times 10^{15}$ kg return to the atmosphere via evaporation.

So, where does the extra $36 \times 10^{15}$ kg y$^{-1}$ of water precipitated over the land come from? And where does it go to? After all, if it stayed on the land, the land would be rapidly flooded. As was discussed earlier, on a global scale a balance is established where the total amount of water entering the atmosphere matches the total amount leaving the atmosphere. So Figure 6.3 must be incomplete; there needs to be an extra water input (by $36 \times 10^{15}$ kg y$^{-1}$) to the atmosphere over the land, as well as some way the extra precipitation ($36 \times 10^{15}$ kg y$^{-1}$) can leave the land reservoir. The missing link is that water in the atmosphere above oceans can

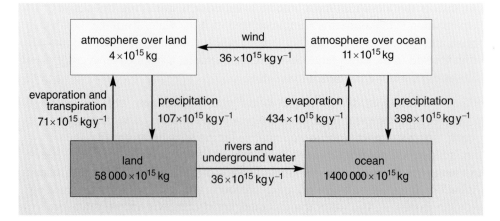

**Figure 6.4** Completed flow diagram of the water cycle. The numbers in the boxes refer to the mass in kilograms of water in that particular reservoir. The numbers on the arrows refer to the movement of water from one reservoir to another in kilograms per year.

be blown by the wind to locations over land, where it can then precipitate onto the land. Furthermore, precipitated water can flow from land to the oceans via rivers and underground water flow. Figure 6.4 includes this extra information which was missing from Figure 6.3.

The cycle shown in Figure 6.4 is a closed loop in which water moves around the system, but the rate at which water enters a reservoir equals the rate at which it leaves it. Therefore, overall there is no change in the total amount of water in any of the reservoirs. The water cycle is thus in a steady state. You will find this is true of many of the cycles you will meet in this course. As in the leaky tank analogy, when in balance, the amount of material in each reservoir is constant even though there is a movement of material into and out of the reservoir.

Figure 6.4 shows the water cycle in terms of only four reservoirs, but some of them can be divided further, more like the categories listed in Table 6.1. The whole water cycle can then be represented as water flowing between all these different reservoirs on a diagram of the land, ocean and atmosphere (as opposed to a flow diagram). This is done in Figure 6.5. Take some time to think about all the possible routes and cycles a water molecule could take, and look back at Table 6.1 to remind yourself how long water might remain in one particular reservoir.

## 6.3   A stable water cycle?

You have been examining the factors that control the amount of water in the atmosphere because water is a greenhouse gas and thus the amount of it in the atmosphere will have a large effect on the Earth's surface temperature.

■  What does the amount of water vapour that air can hold depend on?

☐  The amount of water vapour that air can hold is related to the temperature of the air. Thus the higher the temperature, the more water vapour the atmosphere can hold. You met this concept in Section 4.5.2.

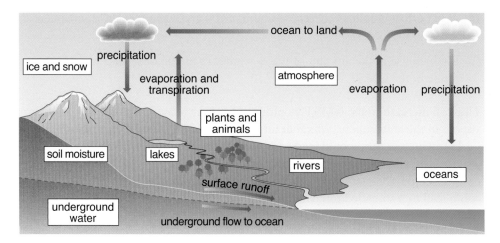

**Figure 6.5**   The complete water cycle. The reservoirs are shown as the white labelled boxes. The arrows indicate the transfers between reservoirs. The blue dashed line indicates the water table, below which the rock is saturated with water.

However, as you also saw in Section 4.5.2, there is a limit to the amount of water vapour that air at a given temperature can hold. When the air becomes saturated (100% relative humidity) it cannot take on any more water vapour. Furthermore, the rate of evaporation is also affected by whether the air is saturated. When air is far from saturation, the rate of evaporation is generally related to the temperature – the hotter it is, the more evaporation there is, which fits with everyday experience. However, as air approaches saturation, it suppresses evaporation, i.e. water vapour cannot enter the saturated air, so there is no evaporation. Thus even in hot conditions (e.g. equatorial regions) the rate of evaporation may be low if the air is already saturated. This might be familiar to you if you have tried to dry clothes in a very hot and humid climate. Clearly then, the highest evaporation rates could occur in a region that is naturally hot *and* dry – a hot desert.

The rates of evaporation, transpiration and precipitation vary with place and time. Also, in any one place, the rates of precipitation and evaporation can vary from one month to the next. This variability in the processes by which water vapour moves into and out of the atmosphere means that, in the short term, the amount of water in the atmosphere varies greatly with time and place. However, in the medium term, the water cycle is close to a steady state, so the mean amount of water in the atmosphere is fairly constant from one year to the next, and there is no significant trend of increasing or decreasing water vapour content in the atmosphere.

Nevertheless, although the cycle may be in a steady state in the medium term, it is possible to identify ways in which the mass of water in each of the reservoirs may be altered in the long term. Just as with the GMST, the stability of the water cycle depends on the timescale over which it is examined. One of the most important factors is the total mass of water held in the atmosphere. Over the long term this could change.

If GMST were to rise, the total mass of water vapour being held in the atmosphere reservoir would increase.

■ What effect would an increased amount of water vapour in the atmosphere have on the GMST?

☐ An increase in the amount of water vapour (a greenhouse gas) would lead to a rise in the GMST.

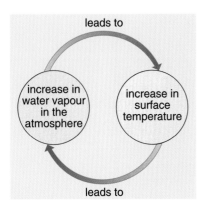

**Figure 6.6** Positive feedback between the GMST and the amount of water in the atmosphere.

Thus, an increase in the GMST would lead to an increase in the amount of water vapour in the atmosphere, which in turn would lead to a further increase in the GMST, which in turn would lead to an increase in the amount of water in the atmosphere, and so on. Thus there are two related factors that promote each other in turn, seemingly ever-increasingly (Figure 6.6). Indeed, this sort of mechanism could lead to a so-called runaway greenhouse effect. This type of behaviour, where a change in one quantity causes changes to others that eventually lead to a further change in the original quantity, is known as **feedback**. In this case, because the changes occur in the same direction, it is called **positive feedback**, i.e. an increase in the original quantity leads to the quantity being increased even further. (Similarly, a *decrease* in a quantity that leads to a further *decrease* is also positive feedback.) In the case of water vapour in the atmosphere, positive feedback seems to lead to an ever-increasing rise in surface temperature – or does it?

There is another type of feedback, called **negative feedback**, in which an *increase* in one quantity leads to changes in others that eventually lead to a *decrease* in the original quantity (or vice versa).

Positive feedback acts to accentuate any initial change. Negative feedback acts to maintain a system in a state of balance.

To familiarise yourself with negative and positive feedback you should now do Activity 6.1.

### Activity 6.1  Positive and negative feedback

We expect this activity will take you approximately 15 minutes.

Figure 6.7 shows a water tank with water entering the tank via a tap and leaving the tank via a pump. The rate at which water enters the tank remains constant but the rate at which water is pumped out of the tank depends on the level of water in the tank. At the start, the rate at which water enters the tank matches the rate at which it is pumped out, so that the level of water in the tank is constant.

(a) Describe what will happen when a bowl of water is added to the tank, if the rate at which the water is pumped out *increases* as the level of water in the tank rises. Is this positive or negative feedback?

(b) Now assume that the rate at which the water is pumped out *decreases* as the level of water in the tank rises. Describe what will happen when a bowl of water is added to the tank, and explain whether this is positive or negative feedback.

Now look at the comments on this activity at the end of this book.

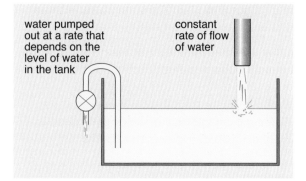

**Figure 6.7** A water tank where the rate at which water is pumped out depends on the level of water in the tank.

Activity 6.1 demonstrates the two types of feedback. With positive feedback, an imbalance drives the system further out of balance, whereas negative feedback returns the system to a state of balance. The water vapour content of the atmosphere is subject to several negative and positive feedback effects, which are relatively poorly understood. For example, an increase in water vapour content could lead to an increase in cloud cover, which could lower the GMST because of clouds reflecting solar radiation back to space. That said, clouds will absorb and re-emit infrared radiation, thus contributing to a temperature increase in a similar way to greenhouse gases; thus increased cloud cover could raise GMST. Overall, the issue of cloud feedback is the least well understood process in global warming and climate change. Therefore, it is not easy to estimate the long-term stability of the atmosphere's water vapour content.

In Chapter 8, you will return to the effects of the atmosphere's water vapour content on the GMST. Before that, however, you will consider the carbon dioxide content of the atmosphere.

## 6.4 Summary of Chapter 6

Water vapour is a greenhouse gas, and thus the amount in the atmosphere is one of the factors that affect the GMST.

Water exists in various environments on Earth – the atmosphere, oceans, ice sheets, etc. – each of which is a reservoir. The transfer of water to and from these reservoirs is called the water cycle.

The water cycle is a dynamic cycle, such that water is continuously being transferred between the various reservoirs. In the steady state, the rates at which water enters and leaves a reservoir are the same, so the amount of water in a reservoir does not change.

The average length of time a molecule stays in a reservoir is known as the residence time.

Over the medium term, the water cycle is effectively in a steady state but, in the long term, the distribution of water among the reservoirs may change. If the amount of water in the atmosphere changes, this alters the contribution of water vapour to the greenhouse effect, which can change the GMST.

When a change in one quantity causes a change to another quantity, which leads to a further change in the original quantity, this is called feedback. If the changes occur in the same direction, i.e. an increase in the original quantity leads to that quantity being increased even further, it is positive feedback. However, if the changes occur in the opposite direction, i.e. an increase in the original quantity leads to that quantity being eventually decreased, it is negative feedback.

The water vapour content of the atmosphere (and the formation of clouds) is subject to several negative and positive feedback effects. Our poor understanding of many of these effects hampers our attempts to understand long-term changes in the GMST.

In studying this chapter, you have read information from a map of the Earth. You have also considered information in the form of flow diagrams. You have had practice in describing the way a system works (the water tank system in Activity 6.1).

# Chapter 7 The carbon cycle

The idea that carbon dioxide ($CO_2$) contributes to the greenhouse effect is not a recent one; it was proposed in the late 19th century. A concept established 50 years earlier is that the global inventory of carbon is cycled over and over in various forms, both living and non-living. Atmospheric $CO_2$ is a vital part of this global **carbon cycle**. In this chapter you will explore the transformations and movement of carbon around this cycle.

## 7.1 The carbon reservoirs

It may seem a bit excessive to study the workings of the entire carbon cycle if, ultimately, the main interest is in atmospheric $CO_2$. The reason for understanding it in full is that, like the water cycle, a change in one reservoir in the carbon cycle can profoundly affect other reservoirs. So, although it may be possible to measure perfectly well the amount of $CO_2$ in the atmosphere now, those measurements alone cannot indicate whether that amount might change over time – in either the short term (days, months, years) or the long term (thousands or millions of years). That requires an understanding of what controls the release of $CO_2$ to the atmosphere from other carbon reservoirs and the removal of $CO_2$ from the atmosphere into other carbon reservoirs. Without some understanding of the entire carbon cycle, therefore, it is impossible to predict how the continued release of $CO_2$ into the atmosphere from anthropogenic (human-induced) sources may change the climate.

You are already aware that $CO_2$ strongly influences the Earth's temperature through the greenhouse effect. Indeed, without $CO_2$ in the atmosphere, the Earth's surface would be frozen solid. However, the significance of carbon extends far beyond its influence on climate. Carbon is the chemical basis for all life on the planet. Every living thing is made of very similar arrangements of carbon atoms linked with each other, and with oxygen and hydrogen atoms (and lesser amounts of nitrogen, phosphorus and other elements). Carbon that is part of living things (organisms) or their remains is usually called **organic carbon**. If all the water was extracted from a plant or animal, the remains would contain about 50% carbon by mass.

■ Carbon is unique among elements in its ability to form literally millions of different compounds (i.e. substances that contain two or more elements). Take a few minutes to make a list of items in everyday life that are composed at least partly of carbon. You could do this by considering your immediate surroundings.

☐ Your list might include carbon dioxide in fizzy drinks, bicarbonate of soda, food, carbon-fibre materials, and anything that is or was living (such as a cat or a wooden table). Less obvious examples are plastics, fabrics, paper, detergents, rubber, drugs, paints, road surfaces and pesticides. In fact, nearly everything is likely to have at least a little carbon in it!

Perhaps you also thought of coal, oil or natural gas. These fossil fuels are the carbon-rich remnants of organisms that lived tens or hundreds of millions of

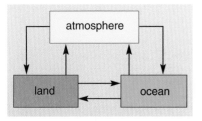

**Figure 7.1** Flow diagram showing the general structure of a global chemical cycle, in which material moves between three major global reservoirs: atmosphere, land and ocean.

years ago. Graphite and diamond are two forms of elemental carbon, i.e. both solids consist solely of carbon atoms (they differ only in the way the atoms are arranged). The Earth's largest reservoir of carbon is in **carbonate rocks** such as limestone, marble and chalk.

Figure 7.1 is a simplified diagram of the global cycle of any chemical substance or element. The arrows depict the movement of the material between the main global reservoirs of atmosphere, land and ocean, just as for the water cycle.

You should recall from Section 6.2, that the movement of material from one reservoir to another can be expressed as a rate, in a unit of mass or volume of the substance per unit of time. For example, in Figure 6.2 you saw that the rate of transfer of water into the atmosphere (by evaporation from land and ocean) is $505 \times 10^{15}$ kg of water per year, which is exactly balanced by the rate of transfer of water out of the atmosphere (by precipitation to land and ocean). When the rates of transfer into and out of a reservoir are equal, the reservoir is in a steady state.

When considering a cycle, you can consider as many reservoirs as you like. For example, the three different representations of the water cycle in Figures 6.2, 6.4 and 6.5 show two, four and eight reservoirs, respectively. None of these three is the right one; they are all equally valid. Similarly, there is no absolute number of carbon reservoirs on Earth; the number of reservoirs can be defined to suit your purpose. An initial, sensible apportionment of the global amount of carbon into the reservoirs could be land, atmosphere and ocean; living and non-living.

However, there is one important difference between reservoirs in the carbon cycle and those in the water cycle. Water remains a single compound ($H_2O$) throughout the entire water cycle. The only changes are where the water is located, and whether it is in solid, liquid or gaseous form. On the other hand, carbon is an element that forms numerous different chemical compounds by combining with other elements, such as hydrogen, oxygen, nitrogen or other carbon atoms. Thus carbon can appear in many different guises, such as carbon dioxide, methane or organic carbon.

Strictly speaking, the carbon cycle encompasses the global distribution and transformations of *all* of the different chemical compounds containing carbon. However, only one or two of the most important carbon compounds in the major reservoirs will be considered here. As you go through the cycle, however, keep in mind that the real world is being simplified. For instance, although the atmospheric reservoir of carbon is considered to be entirely $CO_2$, it also contains small amounts of methane ($CH_4$), carbon monoxide ($CO$), and numerous different, more complex carbon-containing compounds, many of which contribute to the greenhouse effect.

### 7.1.1    Biogeochemical cycles

The global carbon cycle is composed of two interlinked subcycles – a **biological cycle** and a **geochemical cycle**. Together these cycles make up the **biogeochemical cycle** of carbon. Biogeochemical cycles involve the global cycling of the elements that are vital to life, especially carbon, oxygen, nitrogen and sulfur. The elements rearrange themselves into different compounds and move into and out of living and non-living reservoirs. You can think of a biogeochemical cycle, then, as the movement of an element between organisms (bio) and the rest of Earth (geo) through the chemical transformations of that element. Furthermore, any changes in one reservoir will lead to adjustments in other reservoirs, such that the cycle tends to remain in a steady state.

Carbon moves rapidly through some reservoirs, i.e. its residence time is short. In other reservoirs the residence time of carbon is very long. The important point, however, is that carbon is transferring at some rate into and out of all of them. Thus, no part of the cycle exists in isolation. As you will see, changes in one reservoir (e.g. from burning fossil fuels) can have important, but non-obvious, effects elsewhere in the cycle.

You are also part of the global carbon cycle. Chemically you are a very different person now than you were, say, 10 years ago. Most of the carbon atoms that were in your body then are now somewhere else in the global carbon cycle – perhaps the deep ocean, or a rainforest, or a coral reef, or an insect or even another person. Meanwhile you have taken in new carbon in food and incorporated it in your body. The carbon cycle forms a web, binding the living and non-living Earth together.

## 7.2   Overview of the carbon cycle

In this discussion, the carbon cycle will be divided into a total of seven reservoirs. First, four reservoirs within the biological carbon cycle will be considered: carbon in living things, in the atmosphere, in the surface ocean (down to 100–200 m depth), and in soil. Second, three reservoirs within the geochemical cycle will be considered: carbon stored in the deep ocean, in ocean sediment, and in rock.

Note there is a distinction between the surface ocean and the deep ocean. The surface ocean is the layer that receives some solar radiation and is mixed by wind and wave action (usually the top 100–200 m). This mixing allows air to come into contact with the water in this top layer, so that heat, oxygen and carbon dioxide (among other things) are freely exchanged between the atmosphere and this water. This mixing and contact with solar radiation means the surface ocean is fairly warm. Below the surface ocean, the temperature drops steeply until, by about 1 km deep, the water is at a uniform temperature of between about −1 °C and 4 °C (note that the freezing temperature of salt water is below 0 °C). Solar radiation never penetrates the deep ocean so it is completely dark, except for the occasional light from luminescent organisms. There is only limited contact between this cold, deep ocean water and the surface water, so carbon in the deep ocean is to a large extent segregated from carbon in the surface ocean. (The exception to this is in the polar and near-polar regions, where the surface water and deep ocean water mix freely.)

Table 7.1 lists some features of the seven major reservoirs you will consider in the carbon cycle, including the major form and amount of carbon in each reservoir. (It doesn't matter at this stage if some of the forms of carbon don't mean much to you.)

Note that the size of each reservoir in Table 7.1 is expressed in terms of the mass of carbon in a unit of $10^{12}$ kg of carbon, which is abbreviated to $10^{12}$ kgC, a convention that will be adopted for all subsequent discussion of the carbon cycle.

**Table 7.1**  Major reservoirs of the global carbon cycle, showing the amount and major form of carbon, the percentage of the global total mass of carbon, and the mean residence time of carbon for each reservoir. (Note that the atmospheric reservoir value is for 2004.)

| Reservoir | Mass of carbon/ $10^{12}$ kgC | Major form of carbon | Proportion of total mass of carbon/% | Mean residence time/years |
|---|---|---|---|---|
| **Biological cycle** | | | | |
| atmosphere | 800 | carbon dioxide | 0.0016 | 3.6 |
| living things | 560 | organic carbon (living) | 0.0011 | 4.7 |
| surface ocean | 1000 | dissolved carbon | 0.002 | 7.9 |
| soil | 1500 | organic carbon (non-living) | 0.003 | 25 |
| **Geochemical cycle** | | | | |
| deep ocean | 37 000 | dissolved carbon | 0.07 | 1000 |
| ocean sediment | 3000 | carbonate carbon; organic carbon | 0.006 | 5000 |
| rock | 50 000 000 | carbonate carbon; organic carbon | 99.99 | 200 000 000 |

This convention makes it easier to compare the sizes of the various reservoirs (as it did with the water cycle in Chapter 6), but it means the values, although in powers of tens notation, are not in strict scientific notation.

■  Express $37\,000 \times 10^{12}$ kgC in scientific notation.

☐  In scientific notation the value becomes $3.7 \times 10^{16}$ kgC.

The most obvious fact from Table 7.1 is that nearly all of the known carbon on Earth – some 99.99% – is stored in rock. The next point you might notice is that carbon moves around the biological cycle over periods from a few years to decades (i.e. it has short residence times) and the amount of carbon in each reservoir is relatively small. However, carbon moves around the geochemical cycle over periods of thousands to millions of years and the reservoirs are very large. You should also note that the residence times are *mean* residence times. For example, on average an atom of carbon remains in a living thing for 4.7 years. However, if that living thing is a leaf, it may be only weeks or months; if it is a piece of wood, it may be decades or centuries.

The biological and geochemical cycles are linked. This means that a small amount of carbon each year moves from the biological cycle to the geochemical cycle, which is balanced by a small amount moving in the other direction. If you could mark an individual carbon atom, you would probably see it move relatively quickly many times through different reservoirs in the biological cycle before entering the geochemical cycle. It would then probably remain in a reservoir of the geochemical cycle for thousands or millions of years before returning to rapid cycling in the biological cycle.

If 1 ppm of the total carbon in the rock reservoir were moved to the atmosphere, with no compensating transfer of carbon out of the atmosphere, what would be the percentage increase in the mass of carbon in the atmosphere? (*Hint*: using Table 7.1, calculate the number of kilograms of carbon in one-millionth of the rock reservoir, i.e. this is 1 ppm. Then calculate what percentage this mass of carbon is of the original mass of carbon in the atmospheric reservoir. You may assume the values you use in this question are quoted to two significant figures.)

## 7.3 The biological carbon cycle

The biological carbon cycle includes the relatively fast cycling of carbon through living things. Table 7.1 shows that the major reservoirs of the biological carbon cycle are the atmosphere, living things (mainly green plants), the surface ocean, and soil. These reservoirs and the rates of transfer linking them are shown in Figure 7.2.

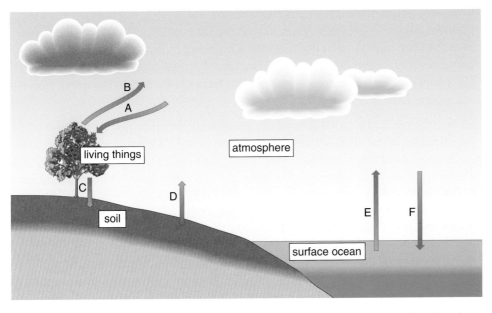

**Figure 7.2** Pictorial representation of the biological carbon cycle, showing the reservoirs soil, surface ocean, atmosphere and living things. The arrows (labelled A–F) indicate the transfer of carbon between these reservoirs.

### Activity 7.1 Flow diagram of the global carbon cycle – Part 1

We expect this activity will take you approximately 30 minutes.

In this activity you will produce your own flow diagram to represent the reservoirs involved in the carbon cycle. You will do this in several stages, adding to the diagram as you meet new reservoirs and transfer processes so that, by the end of Section 7.5, you will have a complete flow diagram for the global carbon cycle. At that point there is an activity that requires you to identify each of the processes whereby carbon is transferred between the reservoirs. To prepare for that activity, keep a list of the processes that correspond to the lettered arrows in Figure 7.2 and subsequent figures as these processes are introduced in the text.

Part I

Use the information in Figure 7.2 to draw a flow diagram for the biological carbon cycle. Use four boxes for the four reservoirs shown, and arrows to represent the transfer of carbon between them. (Don't worry about the position or shape of the boxes – there is no single right way to do this.) Ensure that you label each arrow with the appropriate letter.

Now look at the comments on this part of the activity at the end of this book.

---

You will now consider each of the major reservoirs in the biological carbon cycle in turn, and examine the processes whereby carbon is transferred between them. As you work through this section, you should regularly refer back to Figure 7.2.

## 7.3.1    Living things

Most of the carbon stored in living things is in vegetation. The total mass of *all* living things (plants, animals, microorganisms, etc.) in a given area is called the **biomass**. Biomass is usually expressed as the mass of dry material, or the mass of carbon contained in that dry material. The living things reservoir of carbon is very unevenly spread over the Earth's surface. For example, there is more than 100 times as much biomass on land (mainly trees) as there is in the ocean (mainly microorganisms and seaweed).

Estimating the Earth's total biomass is notoriously difficult, mainly because of the difficulty of calculating the biomass of the world's forests. Currently, the best estimate is about $560 \times 10^{12}$ kgC (the value given in Table 7.1 for living things). This is an enormous mass, but remember that it is spread over the entire surface of the Earth. In fact, it averages out to about 4 kgC per square metre (4 kgC m$^{-2}$) on land. All animals (including humans) account for only $1 \times 10^{12}$ kgC, or less than 0.2% of the total.

■  A good-sized shrub contains roughly 4 kg of carbon. Which areas of the world might contain more plant material in an average square metre and therefore more total carbon stored in plant biomass? Which areas might contain less?

☐  Areas such as forests or swamps might contain more plant biomass and therefore more carbon per square metre. Very cold or very dry areas of Earth have little vegetation and would contain less than 4 kgC m$^{-2}$.

The smallest amounts of biomass per square metre on the Earth's land surface are in lakes and streams (about 0.01 kgC m$^{-2}$), polar regions (0.01 kgC m$^{-2}$), tundra and deserts (each about 0.3 kgC m$^{-2}$). On the other hand, tropical rainforests support an astonishing 20 kgC m$^{-2}$ and agricultural land supports roughly 0.5 kgC m$^{-2}$.

■ In terms of global biomass, what would be the net result of converting large areas of tropical rainforest to agricultural land?

☐ The conversion of tropical rainforest to agricultural land means that less carbon is stored globally in biomass. Therefore, some other reservoir(s) will gain carbon. (Indeed, you will see later in this chapter how deforestation can lead to increases in atmospheric $CO_2$.)

## Photosynthesis and respiration

The role of green plants in the carbon cycle goes far beyond simply storing carbon. **Photosynthesis** is the process by which green plants synthesise organic matter from water and carbon dioxide, using the energy from solar radiation. The process is the source of most of the oxygen in the atmosphere and thus the basis for the existence of virtually all forms of life. Photosynthesis can be summarised as:

carbon dioxide and water, and energy from solar radiation *react to form* organic carbon and oxygen. (7.1)

You should be aware, however, that this summary gives only the overall result – it tells you nothing about the chemical processes involved. Photosynthesis requires many steps, and many complex intermediate chemical compounds are formed. (You will consider photosynthesis in greater detail in Book 5.)

Overall, the process of photosynthesis works as follows. A tiny fraction of the solar radiation that reaches the Earth's surface is absorbed by the leaves of green plants. Water taken in through roots is also transported to leaves, and atmospheric $CO_2$ is taken up through specialised pores called stomata on the undersides of the leaves. In the leaf, the energy from solar radiation is used to split water into hydrogen and oxygen – the oxygen is released from the leaf, and the hydrogen is combined with carbon dioxide to form sugars which releases more oxygen. These sugars are simple organic compounds, containing organic carbon. During this process, part of the energy from sunlight is stored in these compounds, which, in effect, are the plants' food. Further reactions lead to the formation of more complex organic compounds.

Through photosynthesis, then, green plants make their own food from water and air. Carbon dioxide is one of the essential raw materials for photosynthesis; it is drawn out of the atmosphere and into plants. In fact, green plants act as a kind of 'pump' for the carbon cycle; they move carbon from the atmosphere reservoir into the living things reservoir by the process of photosynthesis (Figure 7.2, arrow A). Photosynthesis means that, other than a few minerals from the soil, all of the material that makes a tree or a plant comes either from the atmosphere ($CO_2$) or from rain ($H_2O$). This is why the level of soil in a garden doesn't fall when plants and trees grow in it. (This answers the remaining question posed at the beginning of Chapter 1.)

Question 7.2

Green plants remove approximately $120 \times 10^{12}$ kgC from the atmosphere each year by photosynthesis (i.e. the rate of removal is $120 \times 10^{12}$ kgC $y^{-1}$). The total amount of carbon in the atmosphere is about $800 \times 10^{12}$ kgC (see Table 7.1). Calculate how many years it would take, through photosynthesis, for all of the $CO_2$ in the atmosphere to be removed and stored as organic carbon in green plants, if the atmospheric carbon could not be replaced. (You may assume the values given in this question are quoted to two significant figures.)

The answer to Question 7.2 suggests that photosynthesis would strip the atmosphere of all its $CO_2$ in less than seven years! Clearly, this hasn't happened. A mechanism must exist, then, by which the $CO_2$ removed by green plants is replaced.

Some of the carbon removed from the atmosphere by plants as $CO_2$ is returned by both plants and animals through **respiration** (Figure 7.2, arrow B). This term encompasses the chemical reactions by which an organism breaks down simple organic compounds to release energy. Not even plants can live directly on the energy from the Sun, but must use energy stored in the food they make by photosynthesis. The energy released by respiration is used in maintenance, reproduction, and the growth of plant tissue. The net effect can be expressed in the chemical reaction:

oxygen and organic carbon *react to form* water and carbon dioxide, and energy is released.                                                                         (7.2)

Indeed, this reaction isn't just applicable to plants. It is equally applicable to the burning of fossil fuels (this is explored more fully below). Likewise, the same amount of energy is released from a given mass of food when it is eaten as when it is burned. Indeed, the calorie content of food is determined by burning it.

Like the chemical reaction for photosynthesis, the simple summary of respiration in Reaction 7.2 encompasses several complicated steps. The plate of pasta (organic carbon) you may have eaten last night is broken into smaller and smaller parts through digestion, until it is in the form of simple compounds that can be combined with oxygen (which you breathe in and is in your blood) to release energy for you to continue living. The waste $CO_2$ goes back into your lungs and you breathe it out.

Now, compare the chemical reaction for respiration, 7.2, with that for photosynthesis, 7.1. You can see that respiration is essentially the reverse of photosynthesis; instead of energy, water and carbon dioxide being used to grow plant tissue and produce oxygen, plant tissue is broken down when it reacts with oxygen to yield carbon dioxide, water and energy. Plants acquire energy by breaking down the simple organic compounds (sugars) they have made by photosynthesis. Some animals acquire energy by eating parts of plants; others by eating other animals. In all cases, energy is obtained from the organic compounds in the food, and carbon dioxide is released into the atmosphere.

About half of the carbon taken into plants annually through photosynthesis (Figure 7.2, arrow A) is released back into the atmosphere through plant respiration (Figure 7.2, arrow B).

■ Where does the rest of the carbon go?

☐ The remaining carbon is incorporated into plant tissue.

Most of this carbon goes into building new tissue such as leaves, flowers and seeds; a much smaller amount goes into producing more 'permanent' plant tissue (such as wood, branches and bark) in long-lived species. Around 5–10% is consumed by animals, thus directly (animals eating plants) or indirectly (animals eating animals) supporting nearly all animal life on Earth. Most of these animals (in terms of total mass) are insects.

## 7.3.2 Soil

Nearly all of the carbon stored by plants as plant tissue eventually goes into the soil (Figure 7.2, arrow C). **Soil** is the mixture of mineral and organic material occurring above bedrock on land. (Note that this description of the carbon cycle includes lakes and streams as part of the land and, therefore, lake and stream sediment as soil.) Most of the transfer of carbon from the living things reservoir to the soil reservoir occurs when seasonal vegetation dies or sheds its leaves. However, this transfer also includes the death of long-lived plant species, and the death of animals which eat the plants.

The transfer rate from living organisms to soil is equivalent to about 3–4 kg of fresh plant material (not just carbon) deposited over each square metre of the Earth's land surface each year. Just imagine this happening – it would fairly soon be difficult to get out of the house! Indeed, this is how much material lands, on average, on the Earth's land surface each year. However, it doesn't actually confine people indoors, so where does it go?

The answer, of course, is that the material decomposes. **Decomposition** (arrow D in Figure 7.2) is the gradual disintegration of dead organic matter. Decomposition is simply another word for the respiration of organisms such as worms, beetles, fungi and bacteria, which use dead organic matter to provide energy:

organic matter and oxygen *react to form* carbon dioxide and water, and energy
is released.                                                               (7.3)

Chemically, the results of the processes of decomposition, respiration and burning are the same. The same amount of carbon dioxide, water and energy would be released from a plate of pasta regardless of whether you burned it, ate it or left it to rot.

Now, oxygen-using decomposer organisms can live only where there is an abundant supply of oxygen. This means they must either remain in contact with air that contains enough oxygen to meet their needs, or stay in water with sufficient dissolved oxygen. These environments support a large and diverse group of decomposers. Dig down a few centimetres into pond sediment, marsh bottom or flooded bog, however, and you will be in an area where very little oxygen penetrates, and life forms change dramatically to microscopic organisms that do *not* require oxygen. Here, respiration and decomposition are slowed down, and organic matter gradually accumulates. The consequences of this for the global carbon cycle are explored later.

Globally, the carbon gained by plants through photosynthesis (Figure 7.2, arrow A) today is approximately matched by the carbon lost through respiration and decomposition (Figure 7.2, arrows B and D). The reservoir of carbon in plants does not greatly increase or decrease (although there is a slight imbalance today because of human activities – more of which later). Note that this is a global balance and not necessarily a local balance. At any one place there may be more carbon stored than released (for instance, a rapidly growing forest) or more carbon released than stored (for instance, a decomposing log).

It is worth realising, though, that at some time in the very distant past these transfer rates could not have been in balance, as there were no plants on Earth. As plants then populated Earth, the carbon taken up by photosynthesis must have exceeded the amount of carbon returned to the atmosphere, until the present-day balance mixture of carbon dioxide and oxygen was reached.

### 7.3.3   The atmosphere

The atmosphere is a relatively small reservoir of carbon (Table 7.1) with direct links to all other reservoirs of the biological cycle. Nearly all of the atmospheric carbon exists as the gas carbon dioxide, but makes up only about $3.8 \times 10^{-2}\%$ (380 ppm) of the total number of molecules in the atmosphere.

Photosynthesis in non-tropical regions is most active in the summer (when most plants have leaves), so more carbon (as $CO_2$) may be drawn out of the atmosphere than is replaced by respiration or supplied from other regions. If the rate of removal of $CO_2$ from the atmosphere over a given region exceeds the rate of addition, the mass of atmospheric $CO_2$ over that region will decrease. In winter this pattern is reversed. The effect of this is a strikingly regular oscillation of the $CO_2$ content in the atmosphere over vegetated regions on Earth. An example of this is shown in Figure 7.3. This is clear evidence that the atmosphere and life on the surface are inextricably linked.

■ Figure 7.3 shows a pattern of atmospheric $CO_2$ for a site in the Northern Hemisphere, rising to a peak early in the year, falling in mid-year and rising again at the end of the year. What do you think the annual pattern would look like in the Southern Hemisphere?

□ Summer in the Southern Hemisphere occurs during the Northern Hemisphere's winter, so the pattern of $CO_2$ proportion should be shifted by about 6 months, i.e. falling at the beginning of the year (Southern Hemisphere summer) and rising in the middle of the year (Southern Hemisphere winter).

### 7.3.4   Oceans, rivers and lakes

Unlike the land, where a large amount of carbon is stored in living things, nearly all of the carbon in seawater is contained in compounds dissolved in the water. The main way in which **dissolved carbon** gets into the oceans and fresh waters is via $CO_2$ dissolving from the atmosphere. Fizzy drinks are said to be carbonated (rather than, say, oxygenated, nitrogenated or simply aerated) because carbon

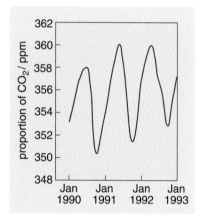

**Figure 7.3**   Proportion of $CO_2$ in the atmosphere (in ppm) measured at about 2 m above the ground at Niwot Ridge, Colorado, USA, 1990–1993. Note that the vertical scale does not begin at zero, for ease in reading the relevant values. The trend cycles from a minimum to a maximum, and back to a minimum, every 12 months.

dioxide is pumped into them to give them their fizz. $CO_2$ dissolves more readily in water than any other common atmospheric gas. (This idea of a gas 'dissolving' may seem strange, but the process of dissolution refers to either a solid *or* a gas going into solution.)

However, like any chemical, $CO_2$ stops dissolving in water when a saturation limit is reached (similar to how air reaches its saturation limit for water vapour). The amount of $CO_2$ that can dissolve in the surface waters of oceans, lakes and rivers is governed by several factors. An important factor is temperature. More $CO_2$ can dissolve in cold water than in warm water. This may seem odd since when you think about dissolving, it is normally solids, such as instant coffee, which clearly dissolve more readily in hot water than in cold water. However, unlike solids, all gases dissolve more readily in cold water than in hot water. Consequently, cold water can hold more of a dissolved gas than hot water (for example, fish may die in ponds during a hot summer partly because warm water cannot hold as much dissolved oxygen as cold water).

At saturation, a dynamic steady state is reached, in which the rate at which $CO_2$ is leaving the atmosphere and dissolving in surface waters equals the rate at which dissolved carbon is leaving the water and entering the atmosphere as $CO_2$. This latter process is an example of the general process of a gas leaving a liquid, which is called **degassing** (it applies to gas leaving a solid too). Gas exchange between the atmosphere and surface ocean is rapid and, overall, the world's oceans are approximately in a steady state with respect to the $CO_2$ in the atmosphere.

■ In terms of the arrows in Figure 7.2, what does this steady state mean?

□ The $CO_2$ released from the ocean to the atmosphere (arrow E in Figure 7.2) must balance the $CO_2$ dissolving from the atmosphere into the ocean (arrow F).

The 'green plants' of the sea are phytoplankton – mostly microscopic algae, which float in the water. The general term **plankton** refers to small, mainly microscopic, free-floating organisms, including some that can photosynthesise (phytoplankton, Figure 7.4a) and some that obtain their food by other means (zooplankton, Figure 7.4b). You may not immediately think of phytoplankton as being like plants, but they photosynthesise in the same way as their counterparts on land. Therefore, just like land plants, they fulfil an important role in the carbon cycle: they remove $CO_2$ from the atmosphere and convert it into solid organic carbon, and release oxygen into the atmosphere.

However, unlike land plants, phytoplankton do not directly remove $CO_2$ from the atmosphere; instead they use 'dissolved carbon' (i.e. carbon compounds, such as $CO_2$, that are dissolved in the ocean water) for photosynthesis. The dissolved carbon is converted into solid particulates or **particulate carbon**, in this case phytoplankton cells, rich in carbon. (Here the meaning of particulate is in the general sense of a small piece of solid matter, whether a phytoplankton, a piece of detritus or faeces.) As the dissolved carbon is removed from the seawater, more $CO_2$ dissolves from the air to replace it. Therefore, phytoplankton indirectly remove $CO_2$ from the atmosphere. In regions of rapid phytoplankton growth, called 'blooms', this effect can be very strong.

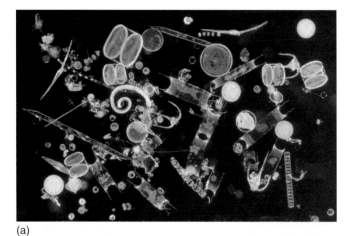

(a)

(b)

**Figure 7.4**   Highly magnified plankton: (a) a 'typical' collection of oceanic phytoplankton (the area shown is about 2 mm across); (b) zooplankton (the area shown is about 6 mm across).

Life in the sea influences atmospheric $CO_2$ in another way besides photosynthesis. Some organisms can combine calcium dissolved in seawater with dissolved carbon to make hard calcium carbonate structures, which are used as external 'skeletons' for support and defence. The most familiar examples are molluscs (soft-bodied, often shelled organisms such as clams, mussels, snails and oysters) and corals. Less familiar, but more numerous, are plankton. Two major groups of plankton that secrete calcium carbonate are extremely abundant in the sea. They are the formidable-sounding *coccolithophores* (a group of phytoplankton, Figure 7.5a) and *foraminifera* (a group of zooplankton, Figure 7.5b). The calcium carbonate formed by these plankton also results in dissolved carbon in seawater being converted into a solid particulate form.

So, for the carbon cycle, the net result of both photosynthesis and calcium carbonate formation in the sea is the transfer of carbon from the dissolved form to a solid particulate form (carbon in organic matter, or carbon in calcium carbonate skeletons). More $CO_2$ dissolves from the atmosphere to replace that which is removed. The effect of these processes is to increase the rate of removal of atmospheric $CO_2$ over some parts of the ocean. Again, the implied balance shown between arrows E and F in Figure 7.2 is global, not local.

Plankton do not live very long: they are eaten or decomposed by other organisms (mainly other plankton) in a matter of days. As with respiration, the net result of this consumption and decomposition is that organic carbon is converted into $CO_2$. In this case, the $CO_2$ dissolves in the seawater. Thus, respiration

**Figure 7.5**   Two families of marine plankton which secrete solid calcium carbonate skeletons: (a) coccolithophores, which are about 10 µm across, and (b) foraminifera, which are about 50 µm across.

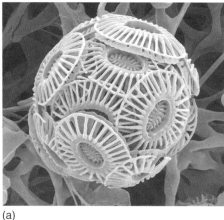

(a)

(b)

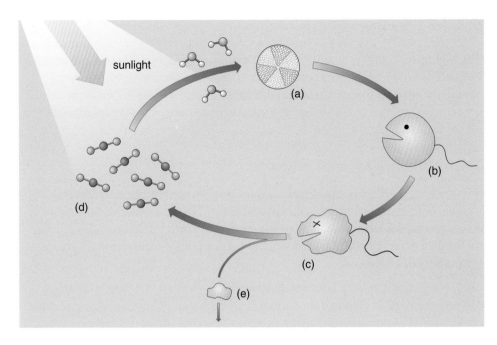

**Figure 7.6** Pictorial representation of the rapid cycling between dissolved and particulate carbon in the surface ocean, through photosynthesis and respiration. (a) Phytoplankton form organic carbon from water and dissolved carbon through photosynthesis. (b) Phytoplankton are consumed by zooplankton and other organisms. (c) These organisms respire, or die and decompose. (d) Particulate carbon from these dead and decomposing organisms is returned to dissolved carbon (here shown as $CO_2$) to be used again in photosynthesis. (e) A small amount of particulate carbon escapes dissolution and drifts downwards.

converts particulate carbon back into dissolved carbon. This dissolved carbon is then available for use by other plankton for photosynthesis or the formation of carbonate skeletons; and so the cycle is repeated (Figure 7.6). Plankton remain in the surface sea, so carbon in the surface sea is continuously cycled from the dissolved to the particulate form and back to the dissolved form.

The matter would end here but for one fact. There is a leak. Carbon in particulates, whether soft tissue, carbonate skeletons, faeces or other detritus, can clump together to form larger masses of loosely bound material. Unlike dissolved carbon and plankton, these sink. These sinking clumps of particulates, which can be large and numerous in areas of high plankton activity, sometimes have a fluffy, cloud-like appearance, earning them the name 'marine snow'. About 10% of the dissolved carbon that is converted into particulate carbon by phytoplankton each year is lost from the surface sea by this steady downward drift of particulates.

The downward drift of clumped particulates is an efficient means of transferring carbon from the atmosphere to the surface ocean and then to the deep ocean. This is known as the **biological pump**, and it is one way in which carbon from the surface ocean is transferred to the deep ocean, and into the long-term geochemical carbon cycle.

### Activity 7.1 (continued)  Flow diagram of the global carbon cycle – Part 2

Make sure that you can name the processes that are responsible for the transfer of carbon represented by each arrow in Figure 7.2 and in your flow diagram. If you are unsure about which processes are involved, you should look at the list that you have been compiling since Part 1 of this activity and then refer back to the appropriate sections of the chapter.

There are no comments on Part 2 of this activity.

## 7.4    The geochemical carbon cycle

The biological pump is a 'leak' from the biological cycle and thus is one of the links between the biological cycle and the long-term geochemical reservoirs of carbon – the deep ocean, ocean sediment and rock. Figure 7.7 adds the geochemical carbon cycle to the biological carbon cycle, thus completing the global carbon cycle.

### 7.4.1    The deep ocean

For humans, the deep ocean (below about 100–200 m from the surface) is a strange, cold, dark and mainly unexplored place. No light penetrates, so there is no photosynthesis. However, the steady supply of particles drifting down from the surface ocean provides a food source that supports a bizarre and diverse community of organisms.

Deep ocean water is very cold (ranging from −1 °C to +4 °C), which means it can hold more dissolved carbon than the same amount of surface seawater. Much of the carbon in downward-drifting particles becomes dissolved carbon in the deep ocean water; organic carbon is consumed and respired as dissolved $CO_2$, and carbonate carbon is physically dissolved. The cold, carbon-rich water slowly circulates around the Earth in deep ocean currents. The reservoir of carbon in the

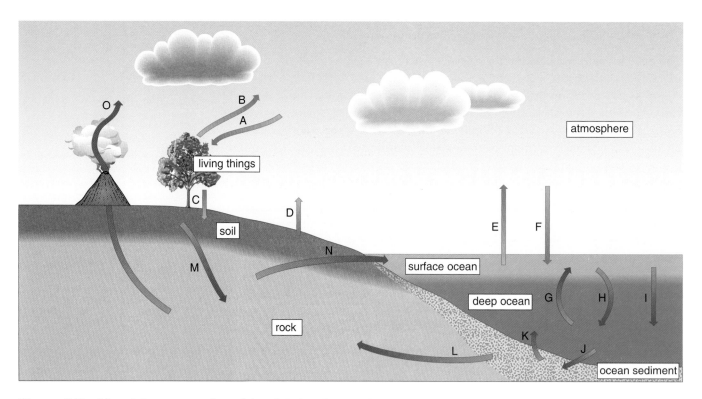

**Figure 7.7**    Pictorial representation of the global carbon cycle, comprising the biological cycle (atmosphere, living things, soil, surface ocean), and the geochemical cycle (deep ocean, ocean sediment, rock). The arrows refer to processes of transfer between the reservoirs: green arrows (A–F) refer to transfers within the biological cycle; brown arrows (G–O) refer to transfers within the geochemical cycle or to links between the two cycles.

deep ocean is large, about $37\,000 \times 10^{12}$ kg, and the average residence time of carbon in the deep ocean is about 1000 years (Table 7.1).

The deep ocean and the surface ocean are to a large extent separate, but carbon does exchange between the two reservoirs through three main processes: downward drift of particulates (described above), upwelling and sinking. (Some water also mixes between the surface ocean and the deep ocean along the broad zone where the two meet.)

Large-scale mixing between deep water and surface water occurs in certain distinct regions of the world's oceans. The large-scale movement of water from the surface ocean to the deep sea is known as **sinking**, and the movement of water from the deep ocean to the surface sea is known as **upwelling**. Sinking occurs primarily in the cold polar and near-polar parts of the world's oceans, where surface water cools, becomes more dense, and sinks to the deep ocean. Upwelling occurs in some equatorial regions and the Antarctic Ocean. The volume of water transferred by upwelling must match the volume transferred by sinking each year, otherwise the relative volumes of the surface ocean and the deep ocean would change (which they don't).

Because the same amount of water is exchanged, and because a given volume of deep water contains more dissolved carbon than the same volume of surface water, about 10% more carbon is moved from the deep ocean to the surface ocean than from the surface ocean to the deep ocean. However, this difference is balanced by the amount of carbon in particulates drifting down from the surface ocean to the deep ocean.

---

### Activity 7.1 (continued)    Flow diagram of the global carbon cycle – Part 3

Add a box labelled 'deep ocean' to your flow diagram, and add arrows to represent the transfer of carbon between this reservoir and the surface ocean. Label the arrows with the appropriate letters.

Now look at the comments on this part of the activity at the end of this book.

---

## 7.4.2   Ocean sediment

A small fraction of the downward-drifting carbon particulates does not dissolve but settles on the ocean floor (Figure 7.7, arrow J). As more material drifts down from above, it buries the earlier deposits. The particulates of organic carbon and carbonate carbon (from calcium carbonate skeletons) form an important part of the **sediment** that covers the floor of both deep oceans and shallow seas. In shallow seas, larger shells and corals made of calcium carbonate can also form part of the sediment, together with the skeletons of plankton and organic matter.

The organic carbon in ocean sediment supports a diverse community of organisms, including those living on the surface of the sediment and those living in the sediment. As a result of respiration by these organisms and the dissolving of some of the carbonate sediment, most of the particulate carbon that settles on the ocean floor is eventually converted back into dissolved carbon (Figure 7.7, arrow K). However, given time and the right conditions, some of the deeply buried carbon-containing particulates may join an immense and exceptionally stable reservoir – rock.

### 7.4.3    Rock

Carbon is moved into the largest reservoir – the rock reservoir – mainly through processes occurring deep below the ocean floor and the land surface.

*Rock formation from ocean sediment*

Imagine that, year after year, more particulates settle on the sea floor, covering already-settled particulates (say, pieces of a carbonate shell or bits of decomposed phytoplankton), and that each year an average depth of 1 mm of new particulates is deposited. A particulate that settled on the sea floor on the day you were born would be covered by only a few centimetres now. However, imagine that millions of years go by. Then the particle can become buried up to several kilometres below the surface of the sea-floor sediment. As this process of burial continues, the weight of the overlying deposits exerts enough pressure to compact the sediment, squeezing out any water and trapped gases. This is accompanied by major chemical changes in the sediment, which are brought about by the heat emanating from the Earth's interior. As a result of compaction and chemical changes, the sediment is converted into rock (**sedimentary rock**). The process by which this transformation is made is called **lithification** (from the Greek word *lithos*, meaning rock) (Figure 7.7, arrow L).

The type of sedimentary rock formed depends on the initial composition of the sediment. Carbonate sediment, composed mainly of the skeletons of carbonate-secreting plankton (Figure 7.5) or, in shallow seas, plankton and corals, becomes carbonate rock such as limestone and chalk. Other types of sedimentary rock containing organic matter – the 'soft bodies' of plankton, faeces and other material – are called organic sedimentary rock. Some of the organic matter in these sediments can, with time, become concentrated to form deposits of oil or other types of fossil fuel. This is why fossil fuel deposits can be considered part of the rock reservoir of carbon.

*Coal formation on land*

There is another major process by which carbon can become part of the rock reservoir – coal formation. Plant material falling on water-saturated soil in peatlands, swamps, marshes and other wetland environments decomposes only very slowly. This stored carbon can be rapidly released as $CO_2$ if oxygen reaches the peat; this can occur, for instance, if the water supply to a wetland is reduced (even temporarily) and the saturated soil dries out. Under the right conditions, however, carbon deposited in wetlands can be stored for a very long time.

The right conditions occurred in abundance some 300 Ma ago when vast swamps blanketed large parts of Earth. Trees living there died and fell into the swamps. There was no oxygen to decompose them, so they remained, were preserved, and became buried by more and more organic material. Eventually, these organic soils were lithified, forming coal and other rocks containing organic carbon (Figure 7.7, arrow M). These ancient trees are burned as coal, and thus release the energy stored by photosynthesis millions of years ago. Today, there is less vegetation on the Earth's surface, and fewer swamps, so organic matter is transferred at a far lower rate to this long-term reservoir.

*The total rock reservoir*

On Earth as a whole, there is approximately four times as much carbonate rock as organic sedimentary rock. Collectively, these rocks are the largest and longest-term reservoir of carbon (Table 7.1). Carbonate rocks store about $40\ 000\ 000 \times 10^{12}$ kgC, by far the largest reservoir of carbon on Earth. Organic sedimentary rocks store about $10\ 000\ 000 \times 10^{12}$ kgC, but only about 0.1% of this is in the form of fossil fuels that are suitable for use as a fuel source. However, compared with some other reservoirs – such as the atmosphere, living things or the ocean – this is still a very large reservoir of carbon.

# 7.5    Return to the biological carbon cycle

You may think that being in rock buried a kilometre or more underground would seal a permanent fate for carbon. However, on Earth, nothing is permanent. You will now consider the final steps in completing the global carbon cycle.

## 7.5.1    Uplifting and weathering

Geological processes, particularly mountain building, may bring the deeply buried organic and carbonate sedimentary rocks to the surface. The process of **uplifting** – pushing deeply buried rocks to the surface during the Earth's movements – occurs over timespans of tens of millions of years, but the net effect, in places such as the Himalayan mountain chain, can be spectacular. You will learn about these processes in detail in Book 2. Here, the concern is more with the consequences for the carbon cycle.

Carbonate rocks that long ago were part of the sediment in an ocean or a shallow sea are very common in some areas of the world; they make up limestone or chalky cliffs (such as the white cliffs of Dover in the UK), many mountains, and chalky or limestone soils. The carbonate rocks quarried today are the fossilised remains of organisms, mainly plankton or corals, that lived millions of years ago. Coal, too, is mined from deposits that either have been exposed at the surface or lie near the surface. These were also pushed up from deposits buried kilometres below the surface by the Earth's movements over geological time. The overlying rocks then undergo **erosion** (the wearing away and *removal* of rock), exposing these once deeply buried deposits.

Once exposed at the surface, rocks are weathered. **Weathering** is the gradual physical and chemical breakdown of rock by water, wind, changing temperatures (freeze and thaw action, for example) and biological activity. Along with other elements, carbon stored in the rock is released, mainly into water (sometimes directly to the air), and thus returns to the biological carbon cycle.

Carbon weathered from rocks makes up the dissolved carbon component of streams and lakes. ('Hard' water, containing high levels of dissolved carbon, is characteristic of regions with limestone – the next time you scrape limescale from the inside of a kettle, think of the carbon that may have recently been liberated from hundreds of millions of years trapped in a limestone rock – and now solidified again in your kettle!) Rivers transport this dissolved carbon to the surface ocean (Figure 7.7, arrow N). Thus, although rivers are only a relatively minor source of dissolved carbon to the surface ocean, they are still vital to the global carbon cycle because they directly link the geochemical and biological cycles.

## 7.5.2  Volcanoes

The other major way in which carbon stored in rock can be returned to the biological carbon cycle is through the rocks melting and releasing carbon directly to the atmosphere. This occurs primarily in volcanoes, where molten rock from the Earth's interior escapes through cracks and fissures in the Earth's crust to erupt on the surface. When rocks containing carbon (as either carbonate or organic carbon) are melted, gases such as carbon dioxide and water vapour are released (Figure 7.7, arrow O). Again, the carbon that was stored in rock is returned to the biological carbon cycle, this time directly as atmospheric $CO_2$.

---

### Activity 7.1 (continued)    Flow diagram of the global carbon cycle – Part 4

Add two final boxes representing the ocean sediment and rock reservoirs to your flow diagram, and draw in arrows to represent the transfer of carbon to and from these reservoirs. Label the arrows with the appropriate letters. You have now completed a seven-reservoir description of the global carbon cycle.

Now look at the comments on this part of the activity at the end of this book.

---

Now that you have covered the main processes for carbon transfer in the carbon cycle, test your identification of them by doing Activity 7.2.

---

### Activity 7.2  Identifying the processes of carbon transfer
We expect this activity will take you approximately 30 minutes.

In this activity you will identify and describe each of the carbon transfer processes in Figure 7.7.

Match each of the arrows A to O in Figure 7.7 with one of the processes listed in Table 7.2. Note that each process should be used only once. Some arrows may be matched by more than one process and, in these cases, you should choose the process that best describes the transfer represented by the arrow.

Carbon exists as different chemical compounds in different reservoirs and, in moving between reservoirs, it is often changed from one form into another. In the third column of Table 7.2, write down a sentence describing the major carbon transformation represented by each process listed. An answer has been suggested for photosynthesis to help you get started.

Try to do this activity first without referring to the text. Then check your answers by referring back through the chapter – your highlighting or notes should have picked out the important points – before comparing your table with the completed table in the comments at the end of this book.

**Table 7.2** Descriptions of various carbon transfer processes in the global carbon cycle.

| Process | Arrow | Carbon transformation |
|---|---|---|
| atmospheric $CO_2$ dissolution | | |
| biological pump | | |
| decomposition | | |
| dissolution and respiration of sediment | | |
| leaf fall and death | | |
| $CO_2$ degassing | | |
| photosynthesis | | $CO_2$ in the atmosphere (or dissolved in water) is converted by photosynthesis into organic carbon in green plants. |
| respiration | | |
| rock formation (land) | | |
| rock formation (ocean) | | |
| sedimentation | | |
| sinking | | |
| upwelling | | |
| volcanism | | |
| weathering | | |

## 7.6    Human impact on cycles in balance

So far the carbon cycle has been considered as approximately in balance. Now you are ready to consider how humans might be disturbing this steady state. The description of the carbon cycle, so far, has only hinted at any possible human impacts but, in fact, humans have affected the carbon cycle strikingly. A glance at Figure 7.8 should convince you that something quite dramatic has been happening to atmospheric $CO_2$ in recent times.

### Question 7.3

Compare Figure 7.8 with Figure 7.3. Both are a record of atmospheric $CO_2$ levels at the same site: Niwot Ridge, Colorado.

(a) How do the scales on the horizontal and vertical axes differ between Figure 7.8 and Figure 7.3, and why?

(b) What is the general trend in the amount of $CO_2$ in the atmosphere between 1968 and 2005 at this site? (Here you are being asked to look at the general trend over the years, rather than the annual fluctuations.)

So, Figure 7.8 shows that the amount of atmospheric $CO_2$ at Niwot Ridge has been rising in recent decades. (Note that this conclusion is drawn despite the gap in the record in 1975 and 1976; scientists are often faced with having to base conclusions on incomplete data.) However, is this upward trend only a local phenomenon? And what was happening before measurements began at Niwot Ridge?

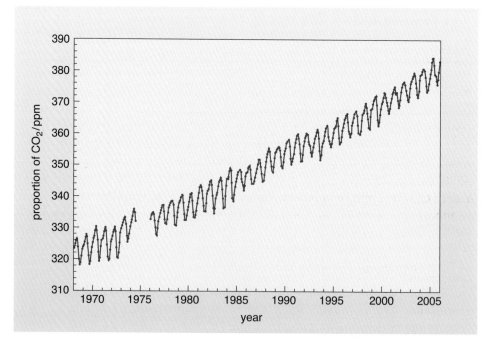

**Figure 7.8**    Monthly record of the proportion of $CO_2$ (in ppm) in the atmosphere at Niwot Ridge, Colorado, for the period 1968–2005.

To answer these questions, perhaps surprisingly, means turning to Antarctica. For many centuries snow has been accumulating there from year to year. As one year's snow is buried beneath the snow that falls in later years, it is gradually compressed and turned into hard ice. Scientists can drill down into the great thicknesses of Antarctic ice and remove cylinders of it as ice cores (Figure 7.9). Careful examination of these cores shows that individual layers of ice, each corresponding to a single year's snowfall, can be identified. Furthermore, by counting down from the top, these individual layers of ice can be dated. (This is rather like dating the annual growth rings in the wood of a tree trunk by counting in from the bark towards the centre.)

**Figure 7.9**  Part of an ice core being recovered from deep Antarctic ice.

When it first falls, snow contains a lot of air. As the snow turns into ice, most of this air escapes. However, as the ice is deeply buried, some of the atmosphere becomes trapped as tiny bubbles in the ice. Thus these bubbles are samples of the Earth's atmosphere from various times in the past. In the laboratory, the proportion of $CO_2$ in these air bubbles can be measured. Therefore, the record of $CO_2$ in the atmosphere can be extended back in time far beyond the records of modern $CO_2$-recording equipment. Figure 7.10 shows the proportion of $CO_2$ in the atmosphere over the past 1000 years, based on the analysis of air trapped in Antarctic ice. The most recent part of the curve (the past 50 years or so) is based on measurements made at the Mauna Loa climate observatory in Hawaii, which has been monitoring $CO_2$ since 1957.

The conclusion is inescapable – the proportion of $CO_2$ in the atmosphere is increasing. As Figure 7.10 clearly shows, the proportion of $CO_2$ in the atmosphere was reasonably constant before 1800 (usually called the pre-industrial level – about 280 ppm). Then from about 1800 onwards, $CO_2$ levels have been increasing (and, as you will see in Chapter 8, are certain to increase every year for many years to come). Furthermore, the rate of increase has been

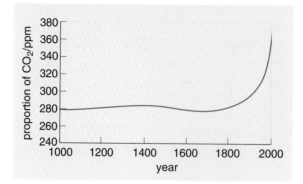

**Figure 7.10**  Proportion of $CO_2$ in the atmosphere (in ppm) over the past 1000 years, as indicated by analysis of air trapped in Antarctic ice, and (in the past 50 years) by direct atmospheric monitoring at the Mauna Loa climate observatory.

increasing over the past 200 years. You can tell this because the slope of the curve gets steeper towards the present day.

Question 7.4

From Figure 7.10, what are the approximate rates of increase, in units of ppm per century, for the atmospheric proportion of $CO_2$ for the periods (a) 1000 to 1700, (b) 1700 to 1900 and (c) 1900 to 2000?

There are no known natural processes that could cause such a dramatic increase in atmospheric $CO_2$ over such a short time. However, the industrial revolution, which involved a huge increase in the use of coal as a source of energy, began in Europe during the late 1700s and early 1800s. Economies all over the world have become increasingly industrialised since then, consuming ever-increasing amounts of fossil fuels. A second human influence is deforestation. Recall that one consequence of converting large areas of tropical rainforest into agricultural land is that less carbon is stored in biomass. When this wood is burned, as is usually the case, the carbon in the wood becomes $CO_2$ in the atmosphere. The rate of deforestation, especially in the tropics, has increased dramatically in recent decades. The pre-industrial level of $CO_2$ was about 280 ppm, whereas in 1998 it had reached 368 ppm, and in 2004 it was 377 ppm.

## Activity 7.3    Updating the $CO_2$ data beyond 2004

We expect this activity will take you approximately 15 minutes.

The data shown in Figure 7.10 extend up to 2000. Clearly, it is important to continue to monitor the levels of $CO_2$ in the atmosphere year by year. Thus you should now retrieve more recent $CO_2$ data from the course website, so you can update the $CO_2$ data set. Do this by carrying out the next two tasks.

Task 1    Obtaining more recent $CO_2$ data

Go to Activity 7.3 on the course website. This page will give you the most up-to-date data available from the Mauna Loa climate observatory.

Task 2    Adding the data to a plot of $CO_2$ concentration

Figure 7.11 shows a subset of the Mauna Loa climate observatory data (i.e. the most recent data from 1994 to 2004), plotted on standard graph paper, with the horizontal axis extending to 2020. Plot points for the more recent data you obtained from the course website, on Figure 7.11. You now have an up-to-date record of the recent variation in atmospheric $CO_2$ concentration.

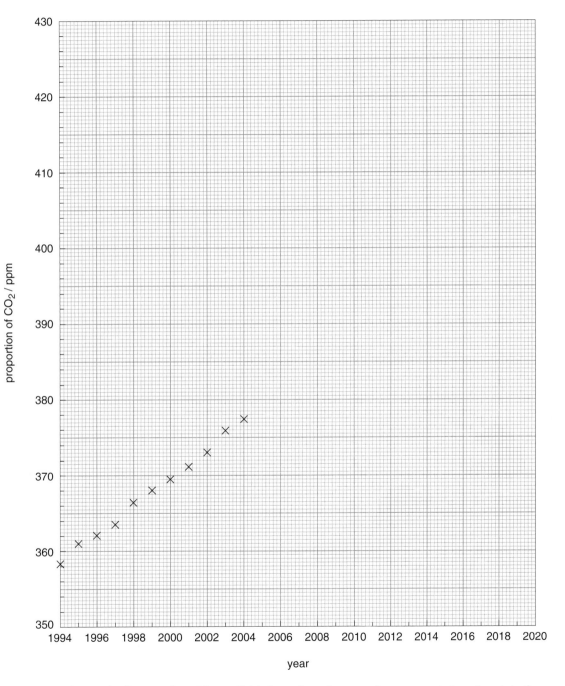

**Figure 7.11**    A similar graph to Figure 7.10, but plotted on graph paper and showing data from only 1994–2004. (For use with Activity 7.3.)

Question 7.5

From the up-to-date Figure 7.11 you have produced, is there any indication that the overall trend of increasing $CO_2$ is continuing beyond 2004?

There are no comments on this activity.

---

So, the amount of $CO_2$ in the atmosphere has increased along with the increased consumption of fossil fuels and the increased clearance of tropical forests. The rate at which anthropogenic carbon is being added to the atmosphere is about $7 \times 10^{12}$ kgC y$^{-1}$, mostly from burning fossil fuels. Of this, only about 40% (about $3 \times 10^{12}$ kgC y$^{-1}$) seems to be accumulating in the atmosphere. The rest must be transferring elsewhere. Current estimates suggest that about $2 \times 10^{12}$ kgC y$^{-1}$ is probably dissolving in the surface ocean. The fate of the 'missing' $1–2 \times 10^{12}$ kgC y$^{-1}$ is not certain, although it seems increasingly likely that it is being temporarily stored in vegetation in the Northern Hemisphere through the increased production and growth of trees. No one knows how long this uptake, if indeed it is occurring, will continue.

Figure 7.12 shows the final version of the carbon cycle – the modern one. Note the two new anthropogenic sources of carbon into the atmosphere: arrow P, which shows the burning of fossil fuels as an extra transfer process from rock to the atmosphere; and arrow Q, which shows the clearing and burning of forests as an extra transfer process from living things to the atmosphere.

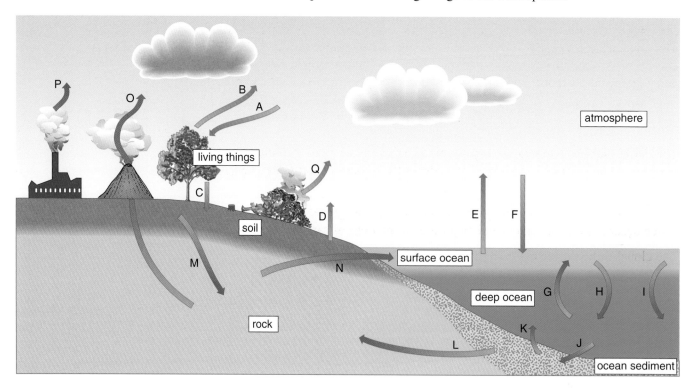

**Figure 7.12**    Pictorial representation of today's carbon cycle. The transfers P and Q represent human-accelerated release of carbon from the rock reservoir to the atmosphere (P) and from the living things reservoir to the atmosphere (Q).

## 7.7   A pause for thought

You have now studied a wide range of science related to global warming. In the next chapter, you will consider the use of 'climate models', which take account of all the effects you have looked at, in order to attempt to predict how the GMST might change in the future. Before moving on, however, this is a good moment to think about all the effects that you have considered so far.

---

### Activity 7.4   Writing a brief summary of earlier chapters

We expect this activity will take you approximately 30 minutes.

When making sense of the large amount of information presented in a book like this one, and when dealing with difficult concepts, it is extremely beneficial to be able to adequately summarise large chunks of text. This activity will help you develop this skill. You should attempt to summarise the key points about global warming from Chapters 2–7. Do this in only a sentence or two for each chapter. Summarising like this is not easy. It requires you to think carefully about the central message of each chapter. Try doing this from memory first. Then look at the summary of each chapter, and pick out one or two of the main ideas from each one.

Now look at the comments on this activity at the end of this book.

---

It is now time to broaden the picture again, and to consider the effect on the GMST of changing not only the atmospheric amounts of water vapour and carbon dioxide but also the other factors that were identified earlier in this book. Moreover, we want *numbers* – we want to be able to determine how much the GMST might vary when a factor changes by a certain amount. In the next chapter you will have the opportunity to do exactly this.

## 7.8   Summary of Chapter 7

The Earth's surface temperature is determined partly by the amount of the greenhouse gas $CO_2$ in the atmosphere. Without the infrared absorption of $CO_2$, the Earth's surface would be much cooler.

The amount of $CO_2$ in the atmosphere is controlled by the global carbon cycle, which describes the movement and major transformations of carbon on Earth.

The global carbon cycle can be broken down into a biological cycle, where carbon moves fairly rapidly through the atmosphere, living things, soil and surface ocean (timescales of years to tens of years), and a geochemical cycle, where carbon moves slowly through the deep ocean, sediment and rock (timescales of thousands to millions of years). Together these cycles form the biogeochemical cycle for carbon.

The atmosphere is a relatively small reservoir of carbon (mostly $CO_2$) with direct links to all of the other reservoirs of the biological cycle and, importantly, to the rock reservoir of the geochemical cycle.

The whole carbon cycle is summarised in Figure 7.12. The details of the transfer processes are summarised in Activity 7.2.

Small changes in either biological or geochemical reservoirs of carbon can have a large effect on the atmospheric content of $CO_2$. This in turn might affect climate through the greenhouse effect. Climate, then, is intimately linked with the living organisms on Earth and with the geological activities of rock formation, mountain building and volcanic activity.

There has been a significant increase in the amount of $CO_2$ in the atmosphere over the last 200 years, the pre-industrial concentration of $CO_2$ being about 280 ppm, whereas by 2004 it had reached 377 ppm. This rise in $CO_2$ is correlated with the onset of major industrial activity releasing $CO_2$ into the atmosphere from the burning of fossil fuels.

In studying this chapter, you have compared information presented in graphical form and made sense of information presented in tables. You have constructed short descriptions of several processes (Activity 7.2). You have reviewed information and have condensed a large quantity of material into a short summary (Activity 7.3). You have constructed a flow diagram (Activity 7.1).

# Chapter 8 Climate prediction

To predict the future climate, or at least the likely change in future GMST, all the processes discussed in Chapters 3–7 must be combined. You have seen that the water ($H_2O$) and carbon dioxide ($CO_2$) content in the atmosphere is critical to understanding the behaviour of the GMST, and the processes that determine the atmospheric content of $H_2O$ and $CO_2$ are complex. In order to calculate the actual amount by which the GMST varies when one or more factors is changed by a specific amount, a 'model' is needed.

## 8.1 Mathematical models

The use of models in science was considered in Section 4.2.1. Models are used when considering complex systems, and approximations and simplifications are made in the models, because it is virtually impossible to account for every little detail in reality. A model then is just a simplified description of something in the real world. By keeping it simple, it is easier to understand and manipulate.

For example, imagine you wanted to determine the combined mass of all human beings on Earth. How would you do this? The reliable way would be to visit every person on the planet, get them to step onto your weighing scales and then, when you've seen everyone, add together all the weights. In reality, this is an impossible task. So, some simplifications are needed. A mathematical model is used to estimate the final answer. In this example, the **mathematical model** could be summarised as:

$$\text{total mass of all humans} = \text{average mass of a human} \times \text{the number of humans on Earth} \tag{8.1}$$

The number of humans on Earth is an input value (or quantity) to the mathematical model. In many cases, the value of input quantities can be measured quite accurately. For example, the current proportion of $CO_2$ in the atmosphere is a quantity that can be measured. If you cannot measure an input value directly, you might have to estimate a value or, indeed, use another model to calculate it. In the simple mathematical model represented by Equation 8.1, input values can be adopted of 60 kg for the average human mass (which is itself a simplification, i.e. a 'model human' is being used), and a world population of 7 billion, or $7 \times 10^9$ humans. Then the mathematical model can be used to calculate the answer:

$$\text{total mass of humans} = 60 \text{ kg} \times 7 \times 10^9 = 4 \times 10^{11} \text{ kg to 1 significant figure}$$

Models are used all the time in science. They are particularly effective in calculating the behaviour of complex systems that have many interacting parts. Mathematical equations are used to describe the behaviour of each part of the model, and computers are used to do the calculations. Hence, the term **computer model** is often used.

In a mathematical **climate model** there are many equations. For example, there is one for calculating the rate at which solar radiation is absorbed by the Earth's surface, and another for calculating the rate at which infrared radiation is emitted by the surface. Moreover, for calculating the GMST, rather than treating the atmosphere as a single entity (reservoir), as in Chapters 6 and 7, it is better to divide it into many horizontal layers, with energy transfers by convection, latent heat and radiation between one layer and the others. More equations are needed to calculate these transfers.

One complication is that the equations are not independent of each other. For example, if there is a change in the rate at which solar radiation is absorbed by the Earth's surface, there will be a consequent change in the rate at which infrared radiation is emitted by the surface. This interaction between equations is called **coupling**. Indeed, each equation is coupled to almost all of the other equations, and so there are not only many equations in the climate model but also a large measure of coupling.

> Coupling can lead to negative or positive feedback. (Feedback was introduced in Section 6.3.)

In a climate model, it isn't the number of equations that go into the model that is the problem so much as the number of times you have to do the calculations. Models tend to change any particular value by a very small amount (perhaps a small step in time) and then recalculate new values for everything using the equations. It then makes another small step, and recalculates again. So the number of calculations ends up being very large, particularly considering that the atmosphere is usually modelled by dividing it into many relatively small individual regions, each requiring their own calculations. In a complex model, the number of calculations is so large that it is not feasible to do the calculations by hand or on a calculator; fast computers are the answer.

Various climate models have been developed to calculate possible changes in the GMST. There are others that, in addition, calculate changes in regional surface temperatures. The variety arises from the complexity of the Earth's climate system, and no mathematical model yet includes all the details. As scientists understand the Earth's systems a little better year by year, and computers become faster and cheaper, more realistic mathematical models can be programmed and run. That said, any model is probably only as good as its most uncertain process. Currently, the biggest uncertainty that climate modellers have is correctly accounting for the formation of cloud and its effects on the infrared transfers in the atmosphere (i.e. accounting for 'cloud feedback'). Consequently, the results from all current climate models are uncertain to some extent.

## 8.2    Global warming and cooling

Shortly you will be asked to do a computer-based activity called *Global Warming and Cooling*. This software package incorporates a climate model that predicts the changes in GMST over the next 20 years or so. You will be able to explore the effect of altering one or more input parameters and see what effects this has. To get the most out of this activity, you need to know something about the climate model it contains.

## 8.2.1  Preparation for the *Global Warming and Cooling* activity

The first stage of *Global Warming and Cooling* calculates the GMST. In broad terms, this model consists of equations for calculating the GMST from all the various globally averaged energy gains and losses that were shown in Figure 4.15, although in the computer model the atmosphere is divided into several horizontal layers. In spite of this, there are no types of energy gain or loss that you have not already met.

Question 8.1

One energy gain is by solar radiation absorbed by the Earth's atmosphere, and one loss is by convection from the Earth's surface. What are the other surface or atmospheric energy gains and losses that determine the GMST?

The energy gains and losses depend on the solar constant, and on various properties of the Earth's atmosphere and surface. The properties that are subject to significant change in the real world are listed in Table 8.1. In *Global Warming and Cooling* you won't be able to change all of these properties – that would be too complex – but you will be able to change most of them.

**Table 8.1**  The main atmospheric and surface properties that determine the GMST and are subject to significant change in the real world.

| Atmospheric properties that affect solar radiation | Atmospheric properties that affect infrared radiation | Surface properties that affect solar radiation |
|---|---|---|
| clouds: cover, type, altitude, thickness | clouds: cover, type, altitude, thickness | albedo of surfaces free of ice and snow |
| aerosols: content, type, altitude | aerosols: content, type, altitude | fraction of surface covered by ice and snow |
| | amount of greenhouse gases ($CO_2$, $H_2O$, etc.) | |

Table 8.1 goes a little beyond the earlier discussion, so you need to consider briefly the entries in the table, starting with clouds. Clouds affect incoming solar radiation through their contribution to the planetary albedo.

■ What is the planetary albedo?

□ It is the fraction of the solar radiation intercepted by the Earth that is scattered and reflected back to space by the atmosphere and the surface. (Albedo was introduced in Section 4.4.)

Clouds also affect infrared radiation. They absorb and re-emit infrared radiation and, consequently, they increase the overall amount of infrared radiation emitted by the atmosphere, which contributes to the greenhouse effect. The overall effect of clouds depends on the fraction of the Earth's surface covered in cloud – the cloud cover – and also on the altitude of the clouds, their thickness, and their type. The type is determined by the details of the liquid or solid water particles that make up the cloud.

Other atmospheric aerosols also affect the planetary albedo and contribute to the absorption and emission of infrared radiation. Note that Table 8.1 follows common practice and lists these other aerosols separately from clouds. Their effect on the planetary albedo and their effect on infrared radiation depend on the size of the particles, their composition, and their location in the atmosphere. Aerosols are produced in many and varied ways, including through human activity. Sometimes an aerosol is released as particles (e.g. smoke and dust) and sometimes the particles form as a result of chemical reactions between atmospheric constituents and emitted gases (e.g. from volcanoes or power stations). In the lower atmosphere (i.e. the troposphere; see Figure 5.2), the residence time is short (days), partly because aerosols act as condensation nuclei for cloud formation, and thus are removed by precipitation. In the 10–50 km altitude region (the stratosphere), which is largely free from clouds, the residence time is several years. Aerosols throughout the atmosphere are only roughly in a steady state and, apart from human activity, volcanoes are an important disturbance. A major volcanic eruption can cause a sufficient increase in stratospheric aerosols to have noticeable, if short-term, effects on global climate (Figure 8.1).

Table 8.1 lists surface properties as affecting only solar radiation. This is because the surface properties that affect the absorption and emission of infrared radiation are not subject to significant change in the real world. By contrast, surface properties that influence solar radiation *are* subject to significant change. It is the contribution that the surface makes to the planetary albedo that is most important. A useful, simple subdivision is to separate the Earth's surface into the fraction

**Figure 8.1**    The explosive eruption of Mount Pinatubo in the Philippines in June 1991 deposited $25 \times 10^9$ kg of aerosol particles into the stratosphere. Over the following year, the haze of aerosols travelled around the world and lowered the mean surface temperature in the Northern Hemisphere by about 0.5 °C.

that is covered in ice and snow and the fraction that is not (which includes the oceans and a variety of landscapes) – this is included in Table 8.1. The albedo of ice and snow shows little variation as a global average and so is not included in Table 8.1. However, the albedo of the surface that is free of ice and snow can vary and so is included in the table.

The second stage of *Global Warming and Cooling* will allow you to explore something that has received scant attention so far; namely, the mean surface temperatures at different places on the Earth's surface. Remember that the GMST is the mean temperature over the whole of the Earth's surface. At a particular location or region, the mean temperature is called simply the mean surface temperature, MST. Obviously, the MST is not the same everywhere, for example, it is lower in polar regions than in equatorial regions. What is not obvious is that a given change in GMST will lead to larger changes in the MST in some places, and smaller changes in others. The model allows you to explore these regional differences. In place of a globally averaged Earth, the Earth in the model is divided into several separate locations (specified by the latitude and longitude of the location) which interact with each other. If you are not familiar with latitude and longitude, or angles, read Box 8.1 now.

---

Box 8.1    Angles, latitude and longitude

Latitude and longitude indicate a location on the Earth using angles to specify a particular place (rather than, for example, distances). An angle is the amount of 'turn' between one direction and another. The unit of angle is the degree or arc, usually just called the degree, symbol °. (Note that it has nothing to do with degree Celsius.)

The angle between two directions that are the same is zero. The angle between two directions that are perpendicular to each other is called a right angle. In degrees, a **right angle** has the value 90°. A complete turn is 360° (i.e. four right angles). Why 360°, and not a 'round number' such as 100? The 360° convention comes from earlier civilisations, notably from the Babylonians who flourished in the Middle East several thousand years ago. They defined a full turn as 360° as this is not very different from the number of days in the year. They used 360 rather than 365, as 360 is more easily divisible – so a right angle is a nice round 90° and not 91.25°!

■    What is the angle in degrees between one direction and the opposite direction?

☐    This is half a full turn or 180° (i.e. two right angles).

An angle that happens not to be a whole number of degrees can, of course, be written in degrees with decimal places (e.g. an angle of 23.89°). However, degrees also have subunits: there are 60 minutes of arc (or simply minutes) in one degree, and there are 60 seconds of arc (or simply seconds) in one minute. An angle can thus be written as degrees, minutes and seconds, for example 23° 53′ 24″ (where ′ denotes minutes, and ″ denotes seconds). This is often how you see latitude and longitude written

**Figure 8.2**  Protractors are usually made of transparent plastic so they can be placed on the page to measure the angle between two lines (or directions). This figure shows an angle of 60° between two lines.

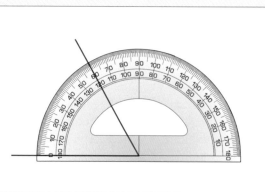

(see below). Although this might seem unfamiliar, it is basically the same as writing the time as hours, minutes and seconds.

A useful device for measuring angles on a diagram is a protractor (Figure 8.2).

Figure 8.3 shows how latitude and longitude are measured by angles. The globe of the Earth has circles of equal latitude running around it, parallel to the Equator, whereas longitude is defined by lines running from one pole to the other. The line of 0° of longitude goes through Greenwich, England.

■ Use Figure 8.3 to estimate the latitude and longitude of London (A), Cairo (B) and Rio de Janeiro (C).

□ London is just over 50° N and about 0° longitude. Cairo is about 30° N and just over 30° E. Rio de Janeiro is about 23° S and just under 45° W.

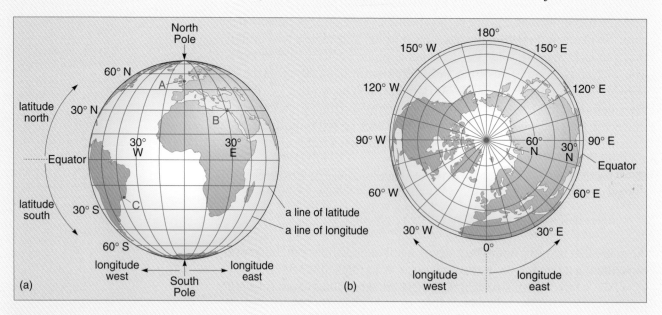

**Figure 8.3**  Geographical globe viewed from (a) above the Equator and (b) above the North Pole. Lines of latitude and longitude are shown at 15° intervals.

You are now ready to use the model in *Global Warming and Cooling*.

---

**Activity 8.1    Global warming and cooling**

We expect this activity will take you approximately 1 hour.

You should now work through the computer-based activity *Global Warming and Cooling*.

This is the first interactive package you have met in the course, and you will be running it on your computer. Go to the *Course Guide* for details of how to do this.

There are no comments on this activity.

---

## 8.2.2    Some reflections on *Global Warming and Cooling*

The climate model in *Global Warming and Cooling* is simplified in several ways so that it can be used to calculate new temperatures in a reasonable amount of computing time. One obvious simplification is that the Earth's surface properties are assumed to have no variation with longitude. Consequently, it was only possible to calculate the MST at different latitudes. In reality, the Earth's surface properties vary greatly with longitude. For example, if you journey west from London, keeping at constant latitude, you cross the Atlantic Ocean, then Canada with its central plains and huge mountain ranges, then the north Pacific Ocean, and so on. These longitude variations in the Earth's surface lead to longitude variations in climate at a fixed latitude. There is a direct effect, in which the climate at a fixed latitude varies with the height of the surface above sea level, and with distance from the sea, and an indirect effect through the influence of winds and ocean currents.

In the activity you also considered the effect of the tilt in the Earth's spin axis. You saw that regions in the Northern and Southern Hemisphere (particularly the poles) can receive different amounts of solar radiation according to the time of year, i.e. this is what causes the seasons. This tilt, which is currently about 23.5°, does in fact vary between 22.2° and 24.4° over periods of about 40 000 years. Furthermore, the Earth's orbit around the Sun changes slightly over periods of about 100 000 years. The orbit can go from a situation where the distance of the Earth from the Sun is almost constant throughout a year to a situation where this distance can vary by about 10% throughout the year. These long-term variations in tilt and orbit affect long-term climate conditions, and have a key role in governing when ice ages occur. You will return to this point in Book 6.

When running the model in *Global Warming and Cooling* you could alter the solar constant. This showed that the GMST was strongly linked to the amount of solar radiation that the Earth receives. Of course, the mean value of the solar constant is not likely to change significantly for a very long time to come. However, it may interest you to know that when the Earth was young, the solar luminosity was only about 70% of the current value. So the Earth received considerably less solar radiation in its early days (although some of this effect would have been counteracted by the fact that the atmosphere on the early Earth had a much higher proportion of $CO_2$ than today and thus a much stronger greenhouse effect).

Question 8.2

A decrease in the solar constant would be expected to lead to an increase in the fraction of the Earth's surface covered by snow and ice. How does the immediate effect on the GMST lead to an example of positive feedback?

There is no doubt that, in general, the more elaborate the model, the more confidence there should be in its results; the Earth's climate system is so complicated that simple models are bound to give inferior results. Although the climate model in *Global Warming and Cooling* is not particularly simple, far more elaborate models exist. Therefore, you might expect that 'state of the art' models run on the world's fastest supercomputers would give accurate predictions of the future GMST. While it is certainly true that climate models have improved greatly over the last 20 years, there are still significant uncertainties in the predictions the models give. Different research groups develop different climate models, which give somewhat different answers. It is simply not possible to get a precise prediction of GMST that is definitely accurate. However, what can be said with some confidence is that the GMST will almost certainly fall between a *range* of values. As models improve and subtleties in the Earth's climate system are better understood (particularly in relation to cloud cover), the range of predicted GMST values might be reduced – but this is by no means certain.

## 8.3    Is global warming anthropogenic?

You have seen that the GMST has been increasing over the past 200 years (Figure 3.7). Furthermore, in Section 3.3.2 you calculated the current rate of increase to be about 0.5 °C per century – a rate that (as you saw in Section 3.4.3) is about five times greater than experienced on Earth in the past as indicated by the temperature record from the Grande Pile core (see Figure 3.16). Thus the current warming does not appear to be natural. That said, you will see in Book 6, that there is evidence of rather rapid changes in the temperature on Earth in the past, so the current warming rate may not be unique.

You have also seen that the proportion of $CO_2$ in the atmosphere has been rising for the past 200 years (see Figure 7.10), in line with the known amounts of $CO_2$ that have been released into the atmosphere from the burning of fossil fuels. The increases in $CO_2$ and GMST appear to be broadly correlated, i.e. they appear to behave in the same way. This is fairly compelling evidence that anthropogenic $CO_2$ is causing the rise in GMST, but it does not prove it, i.e. just because two things are correlated does not mean that one is causing the other.

The closest thing to proof probably comes from using climate models. Figure 8.4a shows the temperature difference between the observed annual GMST and an adopted reference temperature for the past 140 years or so (similar to Figure 3.7). The results obtained by various climate models are also plotted. These results are plotted as a shaded band which represents the range of results obtained from several runs of different models. This shaded band indicates the likely uncertainty in the model results. In Figure 8.4a, the models were run accounting for 'natural' effects only, such as the slight variation in the solar

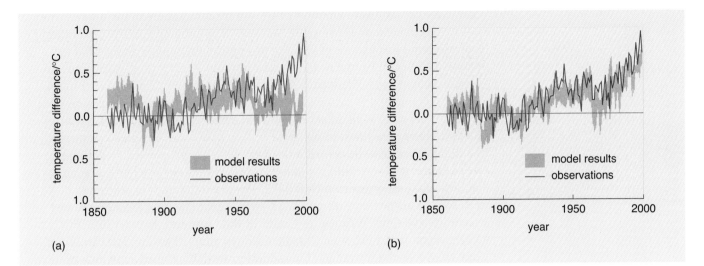

**Figure 8.4**   Results from complex climate models (grey shaded band) that attempt to simulate the observed variations in the Earth's GMST (red line) over the past 140 years: (a) from models run with only natural effects (such as volcanic eruptions and solar constant changes) included in them; (b) from models including anthropogenic greenhouse gases.

constant and known levels of volcanic aerosols, but without including the rise in $CO_2$ concentration (or any other anthropogenic greenhouse gases).

■  Do the model results shown in Figure 8.4a successfully simulate the observations of the GMST?

☐  No; the model does not appear very successful at simulating the observed GMST, particularly the rise in GMST in the last 50 years.

In Figure 8.4b, the models have been run as before, except that now the rise in $CO_2$ levels (and other anthropogenic greenhouse gases) have been included. You can see that the models simulate the GMST data considerably better than before, with the most striking characteristic being that they show the rapid rise in GMST in the last 50 years. These results show that we simply cannot explain the recent observed GMST increase without the anthropogenic greenhouse gases. Furthermore, when the anthropogenic greenhouse gases are included in the models, the results do appear to simulate the observed trends of the GMST data.

For most people, this is evidence enough that human activity is indeed the cause of global warming. Certainly it seems *incredibly* unlikely that some, as yet undiscovered, mechanism will be identified showing that global warming is unrelated to the emission of anthropogenic greenhouse gases.

## 8.4   Predicting the future GMST

The fact that modern climate models can broadly simulate the Earth's GMST over the past 140 years increases confidence that the results they predict for the future are fairly reliable. This means they can be used to predict approximate future GMST with some level of confidence.

First, consider the likely amounts of $CO_2$ in the atmosphere in the future. This will largely depend on the rates of emission of anthropogenic $CO_2$ (and other anthropogenic greenhouse gases). By making an assumption about what the emission rates will be, the resulting concentration of $CO_2$ (and other gases) in the atmosphere can be defined, and the models can then calculate the resulting GMST. Of course, it is extremely hard to know what the carbon emission rates will be. It depends to an extent on political decisions, i.e. the will of countries to reduce their emissions, or not. So a few scenarios (i.e. imagined pictures of the future) need to be considered which describe anthropogenic emissions in the future. It is very unlikely that there will be extreme scenarios, i.e. that carbon emissions either stop completely or vastly increase. Instead, it is sensible to assume that carbon emissions will continue, to a greater or lesser extent – a so-called 'Business as Usual' or BaU scenario. In 2001, the IPCC (Intergovernmental Panel on Climate Change) adopted several BaU emission scenarios, describing a range of possibilities, from continued economic growth based on fossil fuel use, to an economy which is less reliant on fossil fuel and uses many clean, efficient technologies.

Figure 8.5a shows the rates of $CO_2$ emission predicted until 2100 for two of the IPCC's BaU scenarios – two scenarios that might be considered the best and the worst cases. The lower curve shows a scenario where $CO_2$ emissions continue to rise but at a modest rate until, by about 2050, emissions start to fall. The upper curve shows a scenario where $CO_2$ emissions continue to rise steeply, the effect of reduced emissions not happening until the end of the century. Figure 8.5b shows the predicted atmospheric $CO_2$ concentrations that would result from these scenarios.

■ In 2000, the proportion of $CO_2$ in the atmosphere was 370 ppm. Based on Figure 8.5b, what could the proportion of $CO_2$ in the atmosphere be by 2100? (Give a possible range of values.)

□ From Figure 8.5b, the proportion of $CO_2$ in the atmosphere in 2100 might be between about 550 ppm (lower BaU scenario) and about 950 ppm (upper BaU scenario).

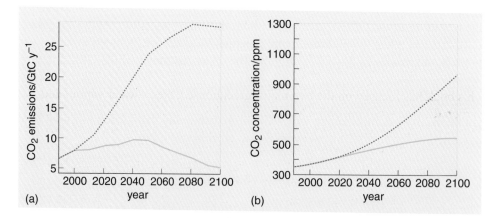

**Figure 8.5**    Two of the IPCC's BaU scenarios. (a) Predicted emission rates until 2100 of $CO_2$ (expressed as GtC $y^{-1}$, where one GtC is $10^{12}$ kgC, and kgC represents kilograms of carbon). (b) Corresponding predicted resulting proportions (in ppm) of $CO_2$ in the atmosphere.

The future probably lies somewhere between the two scenarios in Figure 8.5 but, even so, the proportion of $CO_2$ in the atmosphere in 2100 will certainly be about double what it is currently.

Note that, even in the more optimistic scenario, where emissions peak by 2050 and then start to decrease, the actual proportion of $CO_2$ in the atmosphere would still rise over the next 100 years, before stabilising at about 500 ppm. Although it is not shown in Figure 8.5, it would then take another century or so to significantly reduce the proportion of $CO_2$ in the atmosphere. This demonstrates the time lag between changing the carbon emission rates and the whole system reaching a steady state. It means that a continued rise in carbon emissions over the next few decades will have a lasting effect long into the future. If society does manage to curb its emissions over the next 50 years or so, the $CO_2$ levels will probably stabilise, at a higher level than today, by about 2150.

So, using the sort of information given in Figure 8.5, climate models can be run to predict what the corresponding temperature change (i.e. rise in GMST) would be. This is shown in Figure 8.6 for the two BaU scenarios in Figure 8.5, although they are within a wider shaded area, which represents the full range of results that could be obtained (based on many different runs of different models). From Figure 8.6, you can see that, by 2100, the GMST can be expected to rise anywhere between about 1.5 °C and almost 6 °C (i.e. as indicated by the extremes of the shaded region). Even a 'middle ground' solution predicts a likely rise in GMST of about 3 °C by 2100.

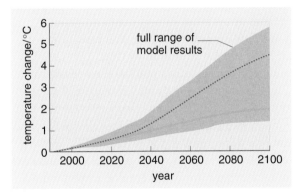

**Figure 8.6**   The predicted temperature (increase in GMST) resulting from models running the BaU scenarios.

### 8.4.1   Might methane have a significant role to play?

This book has focused on the two major greenhouse gases – water vapour and carbon dioxide – but not much has been said about the other greenhouse gases. This is generally because they play a lesser role. For example, the greenhouse gas methane is present in the atmosphere at a concentration of less than 2 ppm, far less than that of carbon dioxide (about 380 ppm). That said, methane ($CH_4$) is a much more potent greenhouse gas than carbon dioxide – given 1 kg of $CO_2$ and 1 kg of $CH_4$, the 1 kg of $CH_4$ would be over 20 times more effective in raising the atmospheric temperature than the $CO_2$. If, for some reason, the proportion of methane in the atmosphere ever increases by a very large amount, it could become an important component in the greenhouse effect.

Could this happen? Currently, there are large amounts of the gas locked up in methane reservoirs. One such reservoir is the frozen subsurface soil (permafrost) of the Arctic tundra, which contains $400 \times 10^{12}$ kgC dissolved in the subsurface ice. If the Arctic tundra permafrost melted as a result of global warming, it could unlock the trapped methane, releasing large amounts of the gas into the atmosphere. This would contribute further to global warming, so melting more tundra and unlocking more methane. This is a positive feedback scenario. Furthermore, this scenario is very sensitive to global warming in that polar regions show much more warming than equatorial regions. Indeed, western Siberia has warmed by about 3 °C over the past 40 years. The effects of this warming are beginning to be seen. In 2006 a region of the tundra spanning $10^6$ km$^2$ (greater than the areas of France and Germany combined) showed signs that the subsurface permafrost was beginning to melt. Indeed, this is the first time there has been any melting since it was initially frozen 11 000 years ago. Scientists will continue to monitor the Arctic tundra very closely in the years to come.

## 8.5    Communicating scientific results

It should be apparent that changes in the GMST of the size – and, more particularly, at the rates – predicted, are bound to have significant effects on human society. Economics, politics and how people live their lives will inevitably be affected. Scientists have a key role to play in global warming, in that they can assess the evidence of what is happening now, and what is likely to happen in the future, and thus inform the debate about what society could do about it. Of course, this can happen only if scientists communicate their results and analyses to the scientific community and the population in general. This links back to Chapter 1, where you considered how scientists publish their results in a peer-reviewed scientific journal, and then these results may be reported more widely in less specialist publications and in the media. Imagine you were the first person to write a computer model much like the one you used in Activity 8.1, and you found that, based on the current rate of increase in the levels of $CO_2$ in the atmosphere, the GMST might be expected to rise by several degrees over the next century. You would want to communicate these important results, so you would write a scientific paper detailing your work, and submit it to a reputable, peer-reviewed journal. Assuming your paper was favourably reviewed by several other scientists (i.e. the appointed 'referees') and accepted for publication, you would hope that the information in your paper would be reported as widely as possible. You could not do it yourself – you would have to rely on newspapers, television news, websites and other media outlets to cover your findings as a news story.

### 8.5.1    Global warming science communicated to the media

This section shows you the process discussed above in action. In the next activity, you will look at a scientific paper on an aspect of global warming, which was published relatively recently in a peer-reviewed journal. You may find it hard to understand some of the paper – after all, it focuses on a specialist area and was written primarily for other specialists working in the same field. Then you will look at how the main results reported in the paper were communicated in more accessible language in the media.

## Activity 8.2  Global warming in the media

We expect this activity will take you approximately 45 minutes.

Go to Activity 8.2 on the course website, where you will look at a scientific paper on an aspect of global warming, and then an article published in the media, reporting the main results from the paper.

There are no comments on this activity.

### 8.5.2  Reporting your rain gauge data to your scientific community

You have seen that communication is a crucial part of science. There is little point making scientific discoveries if no one ever hears about them, and the process starts by reporting the initial scientific results. In this section, you will do exactly that. You will complete the analysis of your rain gauge experiment, and then report your results to your own local 'scientific community' (i.e. other S104 students).

## Activity 2.1 (continued)    Measuring precipitation – Part 3

We expect this activity will take you approximately 15 minutes.

Analysis of results (at the end of week 2)

At this point you have probably gathered two weeks of precipitation data. You can now analyse the week 2 data.

*Task 5    The mean daily precipitation for week 2*

As you did for week 1 (Task 4 at the end of Section 4.8), use the data you entered into Table 2.2 to calculate the precipitation for *each* day measured by the two rain gauges, and enter these values in rows 4 and 6 of the table for week 2. Then calculate the mean daily precipitation in your neighbourhood for week 2 for each gauge and enter the values in the spaces below the table.

There are no comments on this task.

*Task 6    The mean daily precipitation over two weeks*

Use the data you recorded in Table 2.2 to complete Table 8.2, which summarises the precipitation you obtained for week 1 and week 2, and your calculated mean daily precipitation values. Then calculate the mean daily precipitation value over the *two weeks* of measurement, from the mean of your two values. Do this for Gauge 1 and for Gauge 2.

**Table 8.2** Overall precipitation measurements for week 1 and week 2.

| Measurement | Week 1 | Week 2 |
|---|---|---|
| Precipitation for the week from Gauge 1/mm | | |
| Mean daily precipitation for the week from Gauge 1/mm | | |
| Precipitation for the week from Gauge 2/mm | | |
| Mean daily precipitation for the week from Gauge 2/mm | | |

Gauge 1: mean daily precipitation for the complete period .....................

Gauge 2: mean daily precipitation for the complete period .....................

Now look at the comments on Task 6 at the end of this book.

Discussion

*Task 7    Comparing the results from the two rain gauges*

Was there any difference in the mean daily precipitation measured by the two rain gauges? If so, can you account for the difference?

Now look at the comments on Task 7 at the end of this book.

Conclusion

A conclusion to an experiment is a succinct statement (a few sentences) of the outcome of an experiment and how it fits in with or develops our present understanding of a phenomenon.

*Task 8    Writing a conclusion for the experiment*

You should now try to write a conclusion for this experiment.

Now look at the comments on Task 8 at the end of this book.

*Task 9    Reflecting on the practical work*

(a)  Various questions were posed at the start of this activity to get you thinking about how you would carry out the experiment. Did you find that answering these questions helped in deciding how you would do the experiment? In what ways could this 'answering questions' approach be adapted to other practical work or problem solving where you aren't given a list of questions?

(b)  Scientists often present their practical work in a standard format. Quickly scan through the headings that are used in this activity (the earlier parts are in Sections 2.3 and 4.8). Write down general forms of these headings and a brief description of the type of content which would appear in each of these sections. In later practical work, you will be asked to present your results in this way.

Now look at the comments on Task 9 at the end of this book.

Having analysed your data, the next step is to communicate your results to your scientific community. You will do this by posting your results on your online

Tutor Group Forum, so that you and other S104 students can see many different results. You will then discuss possible reasons for the similarities and differences in these results.

## Activity 8.3   Reporting your results to your online tutor group forum

We expect this activity will take you approximately 30 minutes, spread over several days.

You may already have been discussing the design and siting of your rain gauges with other students on your tutor group forum. You should now post your results to this forum.

In reporting the results of your rain gauge experiment, you should include at least the following, to enable other people to make sense of the information:

- the location where the precipitation data was collected
- the period over which the data were collected
- for **each** of your rain gauges (i.e. the open topped one and the one with a funnel), the mean daily precipitation calculated from the two weeks of data and the uncertainty in this value.

You may find it helpful to cut and paste your completed Table 8.2 into your forum message. An electronic version of Table 8.2 is included in the Activity 8.3 instructions on the course website.

You should also comment on any other information that may be important in understanding your results (e.g. the position of your gauges, the design of the rain gauges themselves or any difficulties you encountered in measuring the precipitation which may affect your confidence in your results).

You should compare your rain gauge design and precipitation data with those of other students, and discuss this within your tutor group forum. Why might your results be different (or similar) to those of others?

Now go to Activity 8.3 on the course website.

## 8.6   Summary of Chapter 8

Mathematical models are used to simulate complex systems. They allow quantitative results to be determined about the system. Climate models are one type of mathematical model.

The climate model in *Global Warming and Cooling* shows the general way in which the Earth's surface temperature depends on the solar constant, and on various properties of the Earth's atmosphere and surface.

The aspect of climate models that is least well understood is the formation and effect of cloud cover – this factor more than any other limits the accuracy of climate models.

The amount of $CO_2$ in the atmosphere has increased since the start of the industrial revolution. The GMST has also risen over the same period. Although a correlation between two phenomena does not prove that one causes the other, climate models indicate that the only mechanism that appears to explain the GMST rise is the increase in the amount of anthropogenic $CO_2$ in the atmosphere.

Under even the most optimistic of the Business as Usual (BaU) scenarios used to predict future $CO_2$ emissions, the amount of $CO_2$ in the atmosphere will increase until at least 2100.

The current best estimate from climate models is that the GMST could conceivably rise by anywhere between 1.5 °C and almost 6 °C by 2100.

Although water vapour and carbon dioxide are the main greenhouse gases, the importance of methane could increase dramatically if global warming leads to the release of a large reservoir of methane currently stored in permafrost.

In studying this chapter, you have used a mathematical computer model to understand the various factors that affect global warming, and the coupling between these factors. You have done some practical science, analysed the results and written a conclusion. You have communicated your results to your own scientific community through an online forum.

# Chapter 9  Completing Book 1

In this book you have met several key scientific concepts, including global warming, the greenhouse effect, and the water and carbon cycles. You have seen that the use of models (such as modelling the behaviour of the GMST using the leaky tank analogy and the *Global Warming and Cooling* mathematical computer model) can be extremely useful in describing and understanding the behaviour of complex systems.

Throughout your study of this book (study which you planned in Activity 1.1 and reviewed in Activity 4.3), there have been many opportunities to make sense of information presented in text, illustrations, diagrams, tables, graphs and computer-based media. You have used several mathematical skills and been introduced to qualitative and quantitative data. You have also carried out an experiment (the rain gauge experiment), which included aspects of designing the experimental equipment, taking measurements, recording data, and analysing the data. You have seen why communicating science is important, and you have communicated your rain gauge results to fellow students using an online forum. You have also had opportunities to plot points on a graph, draw flow diagrams and practise writing answers to questions, descriptions, summaries and a conclusion (to the rain gauge experiment).

Throughout this book there have been references to science in everyday life, such as commonly experienced chemical elements, limescale in kettles, carbon in the objects around you, the temperature of the air, floating ice and many others. Linking science concepts to everyday experience allows you to view the world in a slightly different way – a more informed way.

The main theme of this book – global warming – has enabled you to touch on many interdisciplinary areas of science, i.e. you have engaged with topics considered to be biology, physics, chemistry, Earth science and environmental science. We hope that the knowledge and understanding you have gained from Book 1 has enhanced your ability to understand and contribute to informed debate about global warming and climate change.

## 9.1   Your progress towards learning outcomes

In studying Book 1, you didn't just find out a few facts and figures about global warming. You had the opportunity to develop all sorts of skills relevant to being a scientist (as described above). What you are learning in studying this course goes beyond simply the knowledge associated with particular topics, so learning outcomes are used to define what you should be able 'to do' (i.e. demonstrate in assessment) at the end of the course, including all the skills that you will develop. To illustrate this, and to help you monitor your progress towards the course learning outcomes (which are listed in the *Course Guide*), end your study of this book by doing the following activity.

**Activity 9.1  Your progress towards the course learning outcomes**
We expect this activity will take you approximately 15 minutes.

When studying a course, it is extremely useful to have an idea of how you are progressing. Indeed, it would be demoralising if you felt you were not learning anything! However, when considering what you have learned, it can be easy to focus on the knowledge you have gained (i.e. the facts and figures) rather than thinking more broadly about what you can do better now than when you started. This is one reason why there are learning outcomes for the course – they cover much more than just the fact-based knowledge you gain from the course.

Later in the course, you will be asked to use the chapter summaries, and any notes you have made in your study folder, to identify which course learning outcomes you think your study of a book has contributed to. However, at this stage, we would like you to consider *our* attempt at identifying the learning outcomes you have developed in studying Book 1. We have made a suitable template for this activity on the course website, and filled it in accordingly. It lists, in a table, the learning outcomes and where we think you did some work that supported a particular one. A template will be supplied for each book, forming part of your personal study record, and you will be able to add items to your personal record at any time.

One intention of this particular activity is to show you how much you have done in just a few weeks. Furthermore, checking your progress towards learning outcomes throughout the course will help you to consolidate and revise your knowledge and understanding of key concepts, and provide an ongoing record of your skills development.

Now go to Activity 9.1 on the course website.

## 9.2   Looking ahead to Book 2

You have now completed your study of Book 1, which focused on one aspect of the Earth – global warming, and how this affects (and is affected by) the atmosphere, the surface (and near-subsurface) of the Earth, and the life that inhabits the planet. Book 2 *Earth and Space* continues this focus on Earth, but from the point of view of the physical planet under your feet. You will explore the Earth's surface and subsurface, including how rocks are formed, the structure of the Earth, volcanoes, earthquakes, and how the surface changes with time giving rise to ocean floors, continents and mountains. You will consider Earth as a solid rocky planet within the Solar System, and compare it with other bodies in the Solar System. You will also look beyond the Solar System and consider the Earth's place in the Universe as a whole. You will further develop key skills that are appropriate to science, such as plotting data as graphs and interpreting the results. You will also explore in some detail the importance of understanding motion – a key concept in science that applies to everyday experience as well as to the motion of the Earth, the planets and the Universe.

# Answers to questions

Comments on the answers are given in square brackets [...].

### Question 2.1

As the text says, the burning of oil-based products accounts for about 41% of the total emission of anthropogenic carbon dioxide. One-quarter is 25% whereas one-half is 50%, so 41% is closer to 50% than 25% (i.e. it is closer to one-half of the total emission). You may also have concluded this from Figure 2.7.

### Question 2.2

From Table 2.1, the UK's carbon emission is 152 million tonnes of carbon, and the USA's carbon emission is 1580 million tonnes of carbon. Thus the ratio of the UK's emission to that of the USA is 152 million tonnes to 1580 million tonnes, or simply 152 : 1580. By dividing both sides by 152, the ratio can be rewritten as

$1 : \dfrac{1580}{152}$, i.e. 1 : 10.4. So in 2004, the USA emitted approximately 10 times more carbon than the UK.

### Question 3.1

(a) 12.345 6789 rounded to one decimal place is 12.3. (b) 12.345 6789 rounded to two decimal places is 12.35. (c) 3.141 5926 rounded to three decimal places is 3.142. (d) 0.900 999 rounded to four decimal places is 0.9010. (e) 0.999 999 rounded to one decimal place is 1.0.

### Question 3.2

(a) $0.43 + 1.217 = 1.647$, or 1.65 to two decimal places. [Remember that when adding and subtracting, you have to think of *decimal places* rather than significant figures; the number of decimal places in the answer is the same as the smallest number of decimal places in the calculation.]

(b) $8.1 - 3.82 = 4.28$, or 4.3 to one decimal place.

(c) $2.373 \times 3.6 = 8.5428$, or 8.5 to two significant figures. [Remember that when multiplying and dividing, the number of *significant figures* in the answer is the same as the least precise term.]

(d) $6342 \div 2.42$, i.e. $\dfrac{6342}{2.42} = 2620.6611$, or $2.62 \times 10^3$ to three significant figures.

(e) $1111.1 \times 10^4 + 1.1111 \times 10^4 = 1112.2 \times 10^4$ (i.e. $1.1122 \times 10^7$ in proper scientific notation). [Note this answer is obtained in the following way. The numbers $1111.1 \times 10^4$ and $1.1111 \times 10^4$ have the *same* powers of ten, and so $1111.1 \times 10^4 + 1.1111 \times 10^4$ can be written as $(1111.1 + 1.1111) \times 10^4$. The sum $1111.1 + 1.1111 = 1112.2111$ is only justified to one decimal place, i.e. 1112.2. Hence the answer is $1112.2 \times 10^4$. This example was hard – don't feel too bad if you got it wrong!]

Question 3.3

(a) The sum of the mean surface temperatures is 87.3 °C, and there are nine surface locations. Therefore, from Equation 3.1:

$$\text{UK 30-year mean surface temperature} = \frac{87.3\,^\circ\text{C}}{9}$$

$$= 9.70\,^\circ\text{C} \quad \text{(3 significant figures)}$$

$$= 9.7\,^\circ\text{C} \quad \text{(1 decimal place)}$$

[The calculation justifies three significant figures because 9 is an integer and therefore is precise. However, the original figure was quoted to one decimal place (i.e. a precision of $\pm0.1$ °C), thus your answer should also be quoted to one decimal place.]

(b) A more representative value would be obtained if there were more locations, spread uniformly over the UK.

Question 3.4

It is difficult to give an answer to this question because, at the time of writing, we have not seen the more recent data! However, it is expected that more recent data will show a similar year-to-year random variation as the previous data. This makes seeing an overall trend very difficult, until perhaps five or more new data points are added. For now, you can estimate yourself where the smoothed trend curve may lie, and whether there is a continued increase in the GMST. In the long term, however (10 years for example), a continued rise in the GMST trend is expected.

Question 3.5

Figure 3.12 shows several types of pollen. Of the types drawn in Figure 3.11, the most obvious is Scots pine, oak pollen being somewhat harder to identify. These are labelled in Figure 3.19. Two pollen grains that you probably identified as oak, are in fact hazel pollen – but you had no way of knowing this! [Note that a complete reconstruction of the plant population requires the identification and counting of hundreds of pollen grains from a single sample, not just the few grains in Figure 3.12.]

**Figure 3.19**
Identification of pollen grains in Figure 3.12.

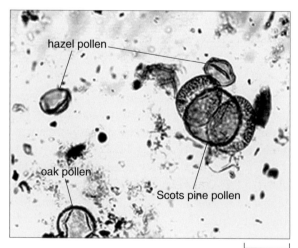

hazel pollen

oak pollen

Scots pine pollen

20 μm

## Question 4.1

Convection involves the upward motion of air in the atmosphere. Pollutants released at ground level are thus carried upwards and diluted, so they do not concentrate near the ground.

## Question 4.2

If there is no convection and no wind, the layer of air next to the ground is not removed. So when the air near the ground becomes saturated through evaporation, this saturated air is not carried away. Thus further evaporation of water from the surface is inhibited. Therefore, the only latent heat extracted from the ground is for the initial evaporation.

## Question 5.1

(a) There are 10 blue particles and 10 red particles, so the total number of particles is 20. In terms of the number of particles, the percentage of each type is $\frac{10}{20} \times 100\% = 50\%$, i.e. 50% blue particles and 50% red particles.

(b) The total mass of blue particles is $10 \times 10$ g, i.e. 100 g. The total mass of red particles is $10 \times 1$ g, i.e. 10 g. The total mass of all particles is thus 100 g + 10 g, i.e. 110 g. In terms of the mass of particles: the percentage of blue particles is $\frac{100}{110} \times 100\% = 91\%$, i.e. 91% blue particles by mass; and the percentage of red particles is $\frac{10}{110} \times 100\% = 9\%$, i.e. 9% red particles by mass. [A useful check is that the percentages add up to 100.]

Clearly, the percentage is different depending on whether the calculation is on the basis of mass or number of particles. [The same problem occurs when baking a cake. For a particular ratio of ingredients, there will be a different result depending on whether the ingredients are measured by mass or by volume. Thus it is important to identify the basis of the calculation or the data since, without this information, the figures can be meaningless.]

## Question 5.2

$H_2O$ has two hydrogen atoms and one oxygen atom; $2H_2O$ has four hydrogen atoms and two oxygen atoms; $C_{12}H_{22}O_{11}$ has 12 carbon atoms, 22 hydrogen atoms and 11 oxygen atoms; $3C_{12}H_{22}O_{11}$ has 36 carbon atoms, 66 hydrogen atoms and 33 oxygen atoms.

## Question 5.3

The atmosphere of Venus is mainly carbon dioxide, which is a greenhouse gas. The atmosphere contains far more molecules per cubic metre than the Earth's atmosphere, so you would expect there to be a greenhouse effect on Venus that is much larger than on Earth. [This expectation is borne out. On Venus there is so much carbon dioxide in the atmosphere that the greenhouse effect increases the GMST by several *hundred* degrees.]

## Question 6.1

(a) If the mean daily precipitation measured in Activity 2.1 fell every day of the year, the annual precipitation would be 365 times the mean daily value. (b) You would have to look at Figure 6.1 to see whether your value is larger or smaller than that given in Figure 6.1. (c) This is unlikely to be the same as your region in Figure 6.1 because the one week you measured may not be typical of the whole year (you may have got 0 mm of rain, for example).

## Question 7.1

From Table 7.1, the rock reservoir contains $50\,000\,000 \times 10^{12}$ kgC; 1 ppm is one-millionth of this, so divide by $1 \times 10^6$, which gives $50 \times 10^{12}$ kgC. The atmospheric reservoir is $800 \times 10^{12}$ kgC, so the percentage increase that an extra $50 \times 10^{12}$ kgC would represent is given by:

$$\frac{50 \times 10^{12}\ \text{kgC}}{800 \times 10^{12}\ \text{kgC}} \times 100\% = 6.3\% \quad \text{(2 significant figures)}$$

[Thus a tiny change in the rock reservoir makes quite a substantial change in the much smaller atmospheric reservoir.]

## Question 7.2

The time taken to remove all of the $CO_2$ through photosynthesis is the total amount in the atmosphere divided by the amount removed each year by photosynthesis:

$$\frac{800 \times 10^{12}\ \text{kgC}}{120 \times 10^{12}\ \text{kgC y}^{-1}} = 6.7\ \text{y} \quad \text{(2 significant figures)}$$

## Question 7.3

(a) Comparison of the horizontal axes shows that Figure 7.8 extends the $CO_2$ record back for 37 years before 2005, whereas Figure 7.3 extends back for only about 3 years before 1993. In Figure 7.8 the vertical scale covers a larger range in order to include the lower proportions of $CO_2$ in earlier years.

(b) The general trend is a steady increase in the amount of atmospheric $CO_2$ over the whole 37-year period shown.

## Question 7.4

(a) The proportion of $CO_2$ in 1000 and 1700 look about the same (i.e. about 280 ppm), thus there was *no* increase, i.e. the rate of increase was 0 ppm per century.

(b) Between 1700 and 1900 the change in the proportion of $CO_2$ was slight but noticeable. The value in 1700 is about 280 ppm, whereas the value in 1900 is *about* 290 ppm. Thus the change is 10 ppm over 200 years (two centuries), which is equivalent to 5 ppm per century.

(c) Between 1900 and 2000 the change in the proportion of $CO_2$ was large, with the rate increasing in the last 50 years (i.e. the curve gets steeper and steeper). The value in 1900 is *about* 290 ppm, whereas the value in 2000 is *about*

370 ppm. Thus the change is 80 ppm over 100 years, i.e. the rate of change is 80 ppm per century.

## Question 7.5

It is difficult to give a precise answer to this question because, at the time of writing, we have not seen the more recent data! However, the data for the proportion of $CO_2$ in the atmosphere shows far smaller year-to-year variations than the GMST data did (see Question 3.4). Thus it is expected that more recent data will show a similar year-to-year increase as displayed by the previous data. Depending on how much data you have, you might be able to consider whether the most recent data appear to simply carry on the trend of the late 1990s and early 2000s, or whether the rate appears to be increasing or decreasing.

## Question 8.1

The other energy gains and losses that determine the GMST are as follows.

*Gains at the Earth's surface*: absorption of solar radiation; absorption of infrared radiation from the Earth's atmosphere.

*Losses from the Earth's surface*: evaporation of water (latent heat); emission of infrared radiation.

*Gains by the atmosphere*: absorption of infrared radiation from the Earth's surface; heat convected from the Earth's surface; condensation of water (latent heat).

*Losses by the atmosphere*: emission of infrared radiation.

[Note that reflection and scattering of radiation are not included; these are not really gains or losses.]

## Question 8.2

If the fraction of Earth covered by ice and snow increases, the planetary albedo increases, so a greater fraction of solar radiation is reflected back to space. The GMST therefore falls. This causes a further increase in the fraction of Earth covered in ice and snow and, hence, a further increase in the global surface albedo, and a further reduction in the GMST. Thus a fall in the GMST causes a further fall in the GMST, which is positive feedback. [Note that this will not go on for ever, even if the GMST stabilises only when the whole Earth is covered by ice and snow.]

# Comments on activities

### Activity 2.1

Task 1

Here are some of the issues that you might have considered when thinking about these questions.

(a) What type of collecting vessel will you use? To collect the precipitation you need a straight-sided container that is sufficiently deep to not overflow between measurements. If the vessel were cone-shaped (Figure 2.10), you would collect water over an area defined by the mouth of the cone, but you would measure the depth of a pool of water that covered a smaller area at the base of the container. So the depth of the water in the container would be greater than the depth that would be measured in a straight-sided container of the size of the mouth of the cone.

**Figure 2.10**   If a cone-shaped vessel was used, it would lead to the measured depth in the vessel being greater than the true precipitation.

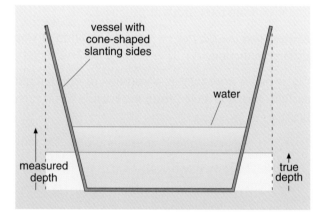

The container that collects the water will be exposed to the air at all times. Did you consider what would happen to the water in the container when the weather is dry? The water will evaporate, just as a puddle of water evaporates, which clearly could lead to measurements that are lower than the actual amount of precipitation. So, you need to take precautions to minimise evaporation from the rain gauge. One possibility is to fit a funnel in the top of the rain gauge as shown in Figure 2.11.

**Figure 2.11**   Two examples of home-made rain gauges: (a) without a funnel; (b) with a funnel.

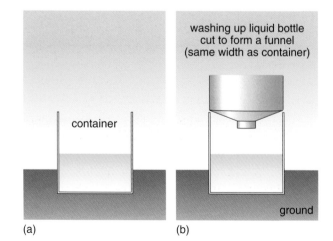

(b) Where will you site the gauge? A rain gauge needs to be placed in an open situation so that it is neither sheltered from the rain by overhanging objects, nor liable to catch drops falling off objects. It will be left out for two weeks (or longer if you are interested in gathering more data – perhaps once a week), so it needs to be stable enough not to blow over easily in the wind or be knocked over by animals. It also needs to be located in a place where people won't trip over it.

(c) How will you measure the amount of precipitation? You will need a ruler or tape measure to measure the depth of the water. You could use a dipstick, as shown in Figure 2.12. If you use a ruler, be sure that you allow for any unmarked length at the end when you record your measurements. You should aim to measure the depths to the nearest half a division (0.5 mm).

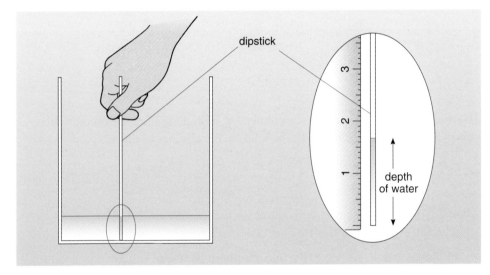

**Figure 2.12**   Using a dipstick to measure the depth of water in a rain gauge.

(d) How often will you record the data? You will calculate the mean daily precipitation over two weeks, so you could simply measure the depth of water at the end of the period and divide by the number of days. However, it is more instructive if you record the amount of precipitation at regular intervals during this period. If possible, you should record the amount of precipitation daily, i.e. over fourteen 24-hour periods. The best way to do this is to measure the depth of the water at a particular time each day.

Do you need to empty the rain gauge each day? You *could* do so, but you don't have to, provided the vessel is in no danger of overflowing. You can determine the depth of water that has fallen in the previous 24 hours by subtracting the previous day's depth from the current depth. We suggest you do this, and empty the rain gauge only if it looks like it will overflow (or else you may decide to empty it at the beginning of the second week).

(e) What problems might you have in measuring the precipitation? If you are measuring in winter, you might have a problem with snow and ice. If there is snow or ice in your rain gauge when you want to take a measurement, you will have to take the gauge inside and allow the snow or ice to thaw. If you are measuring in autumn, you may have a problem with fallen leaves covering the gauge. They will prevent water from collecting and could affect your ability to accurately measure how much water has collected.

Task 4

Table 2.3 shows some typical precipitation data obtained with a home-made rain gauge in Milton Keynes during a week in February 2006. The depth of the water was measured each day, and the depth of water collected in the previous 24 hours was calculated by subtracting the previous day's depth from the current day's depth. The depth of water was estimated to the nearest 0.5 mm, using a ruler with 1 mm markings on the scale. The precision of the measurements was thus estimated to be to ±0.5 mm.

**Table 2.3** Precipitation measured in Milton Keynes in the period 4–10 February 2006.

| Date | 4 Feb 06 | 5 Feb 06 | 6 Feb 06 | 7 Feb 06 | 8 Feb 06 | 9 Feb 06 | 10 Feb 06 |
|---|---|---|---|---|---|---|---|
| Time of recording | 08.01 | 07.56 | 08.04 | 08.01 | 08.00 | 08.03 | 07.59 |
| Depth/mm | 5.5 ± 0.5 | 8.0 ± 0.5 | 12.0 ± 0.5 | 12.0 ± 0.5 | 15.5 ± 0.5 | 18.0 ± 0.5 | 22.0 ± 0.5 |
| Precipitation in previous 24 hours/mm | 5.5 | 2.5 | 4.0 | 0.0 | 3.5 | 2.5 | 4.0 |

The mean daily precipitation is calculated by adding together the precipitation values for each day, and dividing the total by the number of days:

$$\frac{(5.5 + 2.5 + 4.0 + 0.0 + 3.5 + 2.5 + 4.0)\,\text{mm}}{7} = \frac{22.0\,\text{mm}}{7} = 3.14\,\text{mm}$$

Alternatively, use the total precipitation for the week (the 22 mm measured on 10 February), and divide this by 7.

As discussed in Section 3.1.2, the uncertainty in the mean is quoted as a value equal to half a division – in this case, ±0.5 mm. Thus the final answer is quoted as 3.1 mm ± 0.5 mm. [Note that it is not 3.14 mm ± 0.5 mm as the uncertainty is to one decimal place, so using any more precision than this is not justified, i.e. the mean is also quoted to one decimal place.]

Task 6

To obtain the mean daily precipitation for each week, you must divide the total precipitation accumulated over the week by 7 (as in Task 4). This gives you values of the mean daily precipitation for each week. To obtain the overall mean daily precipitation for the period, you need to add together the values of the mean daily precipitation for each week and divide the total by the number of weeks.

You could have left the rain gauge for the complete period, and then divided the total depth of water collected by the total number of days. However, that is risky; if the water spilled just before you measured its depth, you would lose all your data.

Task 7

You probably observed that the depth of water in the open-topped rain gauge (Gauge 1) was less than that in the rain gauge with a funnel (Gauge 2), which can be accounted for by the greater evaporation from Gauge 1. This shows the importance of designing apparatus to minimise possible sources of errors in measurements, such as evaporation in this case.

## Task 8

Here is one student's conclusion.

> I measured the precipitation at Birmingham from 4 February to 17 February, and the mean daily precipitation was 2.9 mm ± 0.5 mm. One of the problems of measuring precipitation is evaporation, and I found that this was reduced by the use of a funnel on top of the rain gauge.

The first sentence reports the outcome of the experiment, i.e. the mean daily precipitation. It also specifies where and when it was recorded. The second sentence reports that the use of a funnel reduced evaporation.

## Task 9   Reflecting on the practical work

(a) Answering the questions at the start of this activity probably helped you to think about how to design the apparatus, and to decide what measurements to make, and may even have led you to think of a few more questions (and answers) of your own. Asking and answering questions is a good way to focus your attention on what you need to do, whether it is planning an experiment, solving a problem, or deciding what you need to learn. When the questions are not given to you in the course material, you should try to develop the habit of devising your own questions to help you with the activity you are tackling.

(b) The order of the practical work throughout this activity is typical of that used by scientists when writing up experiments – a task that you will be asked to do later in the course.

First a title for the activity is given, in this case, 'Measuring precipitation'. Then a general background is given to what you are going to investigate. (Aim and Introduction)

Then there is a description of how to set about the experiment. (Practical procedure, sometimes called Method)

Then you record the measurements that you made. (Obtaining data, sometimes called Results)

Then you work with the data, putting it into a form that gives you the information you want. (Analysis of results)

You discuss what you had done – this might include any criticisms of what you did, how you could improve your experiment, how your results compared with other people's, what you have learned and what you still need to investigate. (Discussion)

Finally, you sum up the outcome of the experiment. (Conclusion)

Note that by doing Activity 2.1 you have learned more than simply how much rain fell over a two-week period – you have learned how to do scientific practical work. You will return to considering how to write up a practical report in Book 3.

## Activity 4.1

(a) When the slot is narrowed, the leak rate decreases. Therefore, the water level rises, which means that the leak rate increases until it again equals the rate of inflow from the tap. The new steady-state level has then been reached, with the water at a higher level, as shown by the diagrams of the tank in Figure 4.19a. The sketch graph shows how the water level changes after the slot is narrowed.

(b) When the slot is widened, the leak rate is larger. Therefore, the water level falls, and with it the leak rate, until the new steady state is reached with the water at a lower level, as shown in Figure 4.19b.

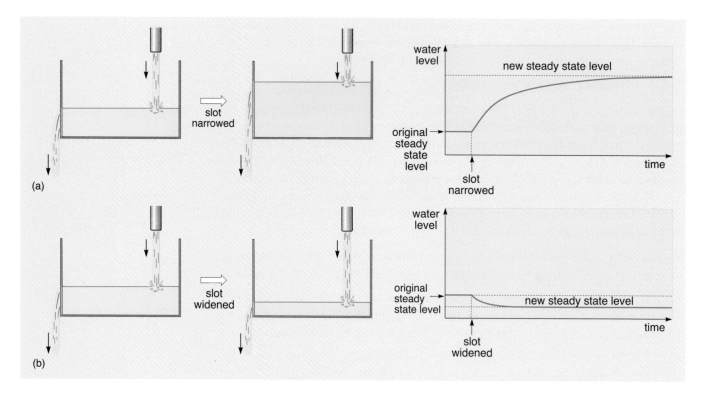

**Figure 4.19**    Changes in the water level in a leaky tank if the input from the tap remains constant but the slot in the tank is (a) narrowed and (b) widened.

You will find it instructive to compare the shapes of the graphs in Figure 4.19 with those in Figures 4.4 (and 4.17 when you meet it in Section 4.7.2), which also show the transition from one steady state to another. In each case, the water level (or GMST) changes most rapidly at first and more slowly as the new steady state is approached.

The leaky tank analogy was used to help you visualise the more abstract changes in the GMST. Thinking of analogies like this is a useful skill to develop. If something in the course text puzzles you, try thinking of an analogy for yourself.

### Activity 4.2

Figure 4.20 shows a completed flow diagram. It contains all of the energy transfers shown in Figure 4.15, but it is laid out in a different way, and the reflection and scattering of solar radiation are shown separately. Your labels may be slightly different but they should convey the same meaning. This kind of flow diagram can act as a useful 'at-a-glance' summary, as can the version in Figure 4.15.

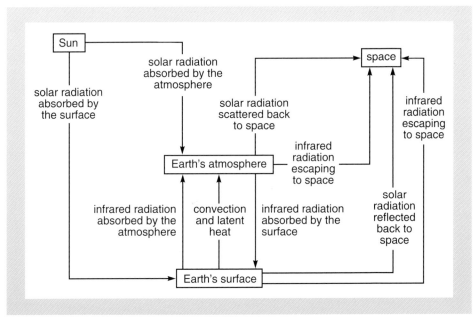

**Figure 4.20** Completed flow diagram for Activity 4.2.

## Activity 4.3

(a) If you suspect you may not have sufficient time to complete your study of Book 1, including the assessment, within the allotted three weeks, ask your tutor for advice. Don't hesitate to make this contact; your tutor will be able to suggest strategies for keeping up with the work.

(b) (i) and (ii) Try to build on what you do well, and don't persist with what is going badly without trying different ways of working. You will find it useful to talk to other S104 students about how they are managing their time and how they are studying the course. Almost certainly you will find that some of them have similar problems to yours, and you will be able to help each other by sharing useful tips.

(c) (i) and (ii) If you have haven't been doing specific things which might be considered 'active reading' (e.g. highlighting text, making notes and summaries, drawing sketches), perhaps you should try it in the next few chapters, and consider how it helps at the end of the book.

Regarding your 'reflection' on these issues (learning methods, progress, etc.), it may be helpful here to know what another student thought about this sort of activity, in which you review how well you are learning. Here is their answer:

> Initially I was annoyed. I wanted to learn science and I thought that some of the activities weren't very helpful ... I find making notes like this difficult but it does help me to understand and remember things. I try to explain things to someone else too. I now discuss the course with my family and friends, and I'm enjoying the course more because of this.

## Activity 5.1

The list below was produced by a member of the course team after reading Chapter 5. You may have omitted some of these points and included some extra ones – there is no single best list.

Composition of the atmosphere:

- nitrogen 78%, oxygen 21%, argon 1%, water 0.5%, carbon dioxide 0.04%
- nitrogen and oxygen molecules have two atoms in each molecule; argon molecules are single atoms
- water and carbon dioxide are chemical compounds, with each molecule containing two different types of atom
- nitrogen, oxygen and argon are not greenhouse gases
- water and carbon dioxide are greenhouse gases because their molecules contain two types of atom – increasing the amounts of these gases in the atmosphere will increase the GMST.

Properties of the atmosphere:

- it is a gas – a mixture of many different individual gases
- collisions of air particles are responsible for air pressure
- air pressure is $1 \times 10^5$ Pa at sea level
- pressure and number of particles per $m^3$ decrease with altitude
- density decreases as temperature increases – this leads to convection
- it reduces solar radiation reaching surface
- it absorbs infrared radiation emitted by surface
- it re-emits infrared radiation
- it allows loss of energy from surface by convection and latent heat.

## Activity 6.1

(a) Before the bowl of water is added, the rate at which water enters the tank matches the rate at which it is pumped out, so the water level is in a steady state. When the bowl of water is added, the level of water in the tank increases, and thus the rate at which water is pumped out increases. Since water is now being pumped out faster than it enters via the tap, the water level falls. The water level continues to fall until it returns to its previous steady-state level, where the rate at which water enters the tank matches the rate at which it leaves.

This is an example of feedback because a change in the water level in the tank leads to a change in the pumping rate, which then leads to a further change in the water level. The initial *increase* in the water level leads to an increase in the pumping rate, which then causes the water level to *decrease*, so this type of feedback is *negative feedback*. The important point about negative feedback is that any initial change causes an effect that counteracts that initial change, so negative feedback helps to maintain a system in a state of balance.

(b) In the second example, the rate at which water enters the tank again initially matches the rate at which it is pumped out. When a bowl of water is added, the level of the water rises, and thus the rate at which water is pumped out decreases.

Since water is now being pumped out more slowly than it enters via the tap, the water level rises further. This causes the pumping rate to decrease even further, and so the water level continues to rise, until it spills over the top, and continues to overflow.

This is another example of feedback because a change in the water level again leads to a change in pumping rate, which leads to a further change in water level. However, this time the initial *increase* in water level leads to a decrease in the pumping rate, so the water level *increases* still further. The initial change and the further change that results from it are both in the same direction, so this is an example of *positive feedback*. The important point about positive feedback is that it accentuates any initial change.

## Activity 7.1

### Part 1

Figure 7.13 shows the flow diagram of the biological carbon cycle. You may have laid out your diagram in a different way, but you should have the same number of arrows entering and leaving each box.

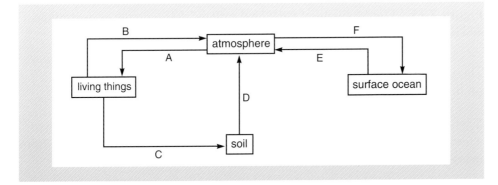

**Figure 7.13**　Flow diagram of the biological carbon cycle.

### Part 3

Figure 7.14 shows the flow diagram of the biological carbon cycle with the deep ocean reservoir added.

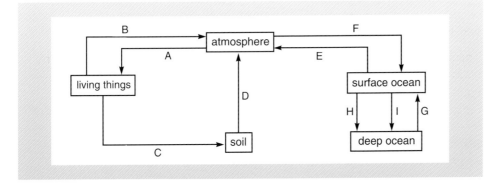

**Figure 7.14**　Flow diagram of the biological carbon cycle with the deep ocean reservoir added.

Part 4

Figure 7.15 shows the final flow diagram with the ocean sediment and rock reservoirs added.

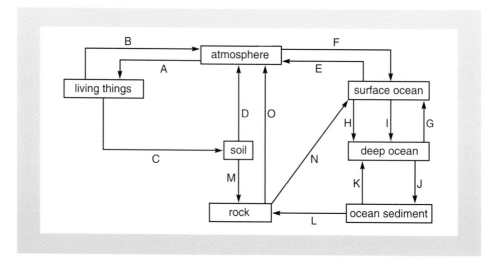

**Figure 7.15**   Flow diagram of the global carbon cycle with the ocean sediment and rock reservoirs added.

This completes your flow diagram for the seven reservoirs that were chosen for this model of the global carbon cycle. In completing Activity 7.1 you have experienced two benefits of producing a flow diagram. Producing the diagram required you to interact with the text, which should have helped you to understand the material. In addition, you have now summarised information from many pages of text into a single diagram.

## Activity 7.2

Table 7.3 shows the completed Table 7.2. The middle column shows which arrow in Figure 7.7 corresponds to each process by which carbon is transferred between the reservoirs. Compare your answers with those in this table. You should have included the same points although your words will be different.

**Table 7.3** Completed Table 7.2.

| Process | Arrow | Carbon transformation |
|---|---|---|
| atmospheric $CO_2$ dissolution | F | Atmospheric $CO_2$ dissolution is the process by which $CO_2$ from the atmosphere dissolves in surface seawater (and freshwater) and becomes dissolved carbon. |
| biological pump | I | Particulate carbon (both organic carbon and carbonate carbon) is transported by the biological pump, from the surface ocean to the deep ocean. |
| decomposition | D | In decomposition, organic carbon in dead organic matter is converted into $CO_2$ in the atmosphere (or dissolved carbon in water) by the respiration of worms, bacteria, etc. |
| dissolution and respiration of sediment | K | Dissolution and respiration of sediment are the processes by which carbonate carbon sediments and organic carbon sediments, respectively, are transformed into dissolved carbon in the deep ocean. |
| leaf fall and death | C | Leaf fall and death is the main process by which living organic carbon stored in vegetation is transferred to dead organic carbon in the soil, either directly or via consumption by animals. |
| $CO_2$ degassing | E | Dissolved carbon in surface seawater (or freshwater) is released by degassing into the atmosphere as $CO_2$. |
| photosynthesis | A | $CO_2$ in the atmosphere (or dissolved in water) is converted by photosynthesis into organic carbon in green plants. |
| respiration | B | Respiration is the process by which organic carbon in living organic matter is converted into $CO_2$, releasing stored energy. |
| rock formation (land) | M | Rock formation (land) is the process by which deeply buried (mostly organic) carbon from undecomposed vegetation becomes lithified (converted into organic rock). |
| rock formation (ocean) | L | Rock formation (ocean) is the process by which organic carbon or carbonate in sediments is converted into organic sedimentary rock or carbonate rock. |
| sedimentation | J | Sedimentation is the process by which particulate carbon from the deep ocean is transferred to organic and carbonate sediments. |
| sinking | H | Dissolved carbon in the surface ocean is transported by sinking into the deep ocean. |
| upwelling | G | Upwelling is the process by which dissolved carbon is transferred from the deep ocean into the surface ocean. |
| volcanism | O | Organic and carbonate carbon stored in rock is released by volcanism into the atmosphere as $CO_2$. |
| weathering | N | Weathering is the process by which carbonate or organic carbon in rock is broken down so it can be transported away (eroded), initially to streams and lakes, and from there to the surface ocean as dissolved carbon. |

**Activity 7.4**

Here is an example of the sort of summary you might have written.

Rises in the GMST of just a few degrees Celsius could have significant consequences for human life and for life in general (Chapter 2). The GMST has varied in the past, part of the evidence being the significant effect that these variations have had on living things (Chapter 3). The Earth's GMST is affected by how the surface and the atmosphere gain and lose energy. In particular, the atmosphere absorbs and re-emits infrared radiation, and gives rise to the Earth's greenhouse effect (Chapter 4). Water vapour and carbon dioxide are the major greenhouse gases in the Earth's atmosphere (Chapter 5). The amounts of water vapour and carbon dioxide in the atmosphere are determined by the water cycle and the carbon cycle. Although there are stabilising mechanisms (feedback), these amounts can change significantly and, therefore, so can the GMST (Chapters 6 and 7).

# Acknowledgements

The S104 course team gratefully acknowledges the contributions of the S103 *Discovering science* course team and of its predecessors.

Grateful acknowledgement is made to the following sources for permission to reproduce material in this book.

## Figures

Cover: Eric Heller/Science Photo Library;

Figure 1.1: Courtesy of Neil McBride;

Figure 2.1: *The Independent*, *The Guardian*, and *The Observer*; Figure 2.2: Rui Vieira/PA/EMPICS; Figure 2.3: Courtesy of Neil McBride; Figure 2.4: MODIS images courtesy of NASA's Terra satellite, supplied by Ted Scambos, National Snow and Ice Data Center, University of Colorado, Boulder, USA; Figure 2.6: United Kingdom Climate Change Impacts Review for the Department of the Environment (1991), *The Potential Effects of Climate Change in the United Kingdom*, Crown copyright material is reproduced under Class Licence No C01W0000065 by permission of Controller of HMSO and the Queen's Printer for Scotland;

Figure 3.1: © Crown copyright, (1990) The Met Office; Figure 3.5: Courtesy of the University of Oxford, School of Geography; Figure 3.9a: Charlotte Thege/Still Pictures; Figure 3.9b: Byran and Cherry Alexander Photography; Figure 3.10: Courtesy of Professor R.A. Spicer; Figures 3.12 and 3.19: Courtesy of C. Turner; Figure 3.13a: Courtesy of C.J. Hawksworth; Figure 3.14: West, R.G. (1977) *Pleistocene Geology and Biology*, (2nd edn), p. 362, reprinted by permission of Addison Wesley Longman Limited; Figure 3.15: Woillard, G. (1979), 'Abrupt end of the last interglacial S.S in North-East France', *Nature*, vol. 281, reprinted with permission from *Nature* © Macmillan Magazines Ltd; Figure 3.16: Guiot, J., Pons, A., DeBeaulieu, J.L. and Reille, M. (1989) 'A 140,000-year continental climate reconstruction from two European pollen records', *Nature*, vol. 338, p. 309–13, © 1989, Macmillian Magazines Ltd: Figure 3.17: Geoscience Features Picture Library; Figure 3.18: Brown, G., Hawkesworth, C.J. and Wilson, R.C.L. (1992) 'A generalized temperature history of the Earth relative to the current GMST', *Understanding the Earth*, Cambridge University Press;

Figure 4.11: David Hancock/Alamy;

Figure 7.4a: Norman Nicol/Natural Visions; Figure 7.4b: Norman Nicol/Natural Visions; Figure 7.5a: Markus Geisen and Jeremy Young, The Natural History Museum, London; Figure 7.5b: Unknown source; Figure 7.9: British Antarctic Survey/Science Photo Library; Figure 7.10: Adapted from Climate Change 2001–1, Intergovernmental Panel on Climate Change;

Figure 8.1: Copyright © US Geological Survey; Figure 8.4: © GRID-Arendal; Figure 8.5: Houghton, J.T. et al. (2001) 'Climate Change 2001,' The Scientific Basis, Intergovernmental Panel on Climate Change; Figure 8.6: © copyright GRID-Arendal;

Every effort has been made to contact copyright holders. If any have been inadvertently overlooked the publishers will be pleased to make the necessary arrangements at the first opportunity.

# Index

Entries and page numbers in **bold type** refer to key words that are printed in **bold** in the text and that are defined in the Glossary. Where the page number is given in *italics*, the index information is carried mainly or wholly in an illustration, table or box.